Talking About Selfbuild

Also by Robert Matthews
PRACTICAL HOUSE BUILDING: a manual for the selfbuilder

The front cover shows the chimney of Rita Blooman's bungalow, decorated for a 'topping out' ceremony (Chapter 1)

TALKING ABOUT SELFBUILD

Compiled and written by

Robert Matthews

Published by Blackberry Books
10 Bartholomew Street, Leicester, LE2 1FA
1990

British Library Cataloguing-In-Publication Data:

Matthews, Robert
Talking about selfbuild
1. Great Britain, Residences, Construction
I. Title 690'.8'0941

ISBN 0–9515295–0–1

Illustrations by Sarah Geeves

**Typeset direct from Author's disc by Saxon Printing Ltd, Derby
Printed in Great Britain by Billing & Sons Ltd, Worcester**

TO MY MOTHER AND FATHER

CONTENTS

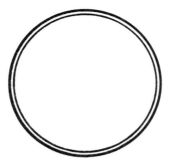

PREFACE

IT HAS BECOME something of a tradition for books on selfbuild to illustrate the topic with some case studies. And a very sensible tradition it is too, for a few case histories soon show what diversity there is within selfbuild.

While I was writing the book *Practical House Building: a manual for the selfbuilder*, I thought I would follow this tradition and so went out to interview some selfbuilders. It soon became apparent that their exploits were so interesting, and all so different, that they deserved a book in themselves. Here is that book.

The case studies are in the form of in-depth interviews, transcribed from tape recordings. They are the stories of the selfbuilders in their own words. Their words not only tell of many adventures in selfbuild, but also, through them there can be glimpsed some special characters.

The book gives, I hope, the real feel of what selfbuild is like: the highs and the lows, the achievements and the disappointments. The course of selfbuild often contains struggles, but invariably it finishes with success. The reader who is attracted to the idea, but who is a little unsure of what is involved, should find many of his or her queries answered. In particular, those favourite questions, "How long does it take?" and "How much do you save?", are well discussed. And some issues are raised that might be unexpected: the effects of selfbuild on family life, for example. Certainly, the wide variety of approach to selfbuild is well reflected in the interviews.

The book also contains, in passing, some useful technical information. Little attempt is made to explain this in detail, but just becoming familiar with the words used and the ideas implied can be helpful to the novice. (There is a glossary of the technical words at the back of the book.) The reader more experienced in building matters should find the technical points of interest.

These interviews with selfbuilders form the core of the book. In addition, there are two further parts:

I have myself done a couple of selfbuilds – a bungalow, built completely by myself, and a house, built mainly with subcontracted labour. Diaries of these builds are included. They may be useful to readers wanting to have some idea of how long the different operations take, their costs, and so on. I also take a look at a commercial builder, and show that it's not difficult for a selfbuilder to build to a better standard.

The book is rounded off with a couple of interviews with people who are commercially involved with selfbuild. They have useful knowledge and experience to pass on, especially in their fields of house-building packages and selfbuild consultancy.

As people who have done it know, selfbuild is often a hard experience. This is not a book for people who want rose-tinted reading. Rather, it's a collection of realistic accounts for those who might really want to get out there and get down to it!

Finally, I must take this opportunity to thank all the contributors who have given so freely of their time. It is their stories which make the book!

RM – Kinoulton, Nottinghamshire, October 1989.

PART ONE

SELFBUILDERS SPEAKING

PART ONE is a collection of eight interviews with selfbuilders. The diversity of selfbuild is well illustrated:

Some people built all alone, some as couples, and some in groups. Some did virtually all the work themselves, most subcontracted some, and one subcontracted everything. The techniques of construction varied too. Some built in the orthodox brick-and-block style, some in prefabricated timber-frame, and in one case, a post-and-beam technique was used, designed to be especially easy for selfbuilders. Some were able to finance their project entirely from their own resources; others had virtually no capital of their own to contribute.

The people interviewed had two main motives for selfbuild. One was an intrinsic interest in making things – and building your home must be the ultimate in this respect. The other was to increase their wealth, and generally this was realized as being able to live in a better home than they could otherwise afford. Most contributors had a combination of both motives.

Despite the diversity of approach, the selfbuilders' stories show some common themes. Most basic is the need for hard work and perseverance. Especially for selfbuilders doing it for the first time, difficulties abound. In wet weather – not uncommon! – the worst often comes first as the selfbuilder struggles to 'get out of the ground'. Even without any particular difficulties, the whole process is invariably a slog. Nonetheless, some people do enjoy it!

Whilst selfbuilding, people's lifestyles have to change. And so another theme to emerge in the interviews is that selfbuild affects family life. The enterprise-in-common can help to strengthen the bonds within a marriage. On the other hand, if there are cracks within the marriage, the onerous nature of the project can drive spouses further apart. And children may be getting less attention then they need.

Despite these hazards, these interviews show that selfbuild is generally a time of special worth and significance in people's lives.

☆   ☆   ☆   ☆   ☆

Perhaps I should say a few words about the interviews themselves:

The interviews were tape recorded and then transcribed onto paper. I edited them a little to make them more readable – spoken words can sometimes appear unintelligible when written down. Nonetheless, the intention has been to retain the spoken nature of the words, rather than translate everything into 'literary' English. The scripts were also vetted by the contributors, who invariably took out their more 'colourful' language. They also sometimes took out their more provocative statements. This, for example, was said about architects' certificates – "Money for old rope". Despite some instances of second thoughts like this, these accounts are, in general, remarkably frank. They record both the pains and the pleasures of selfbuild.

THE LADY BUILDER

THE BUILDING INDUSTRY is still very much a man's world, even if, these days, there are a few women to be found in it: counter staff in builders' merchants, building inspectors, even the occasional site worker. Rita Blooman was not deterred. She wanted to build herself a bungalow, and she built it. When I visited, she was just putting in the last few finishing touches, four years after starting on the foundations. Some people say they have built a house when in fact what they have done is organize others to build it for them. Not Rita. Most of the work she did herself.

Yet she'd had no building experience beforehand. She'd been a journalist, mother and school teacher. Her journalistic experience, though, must have been useful when she visited building sites to glean as much information as she could on how to build a house. And being a woman seems to have been a positive advantage in getting advice and help from tradesmen.

She's a keen gardener, and her garden, though small, was already well stocked with flowers, vegetables and fruit when I visited her in Hornsea, North Humberside (or 'East Yorkshire' as Rita calls it). During our interview, she gave me some pie, home-made of course, with home-grown gooseberries.

Whilst building her bungalow, she lived on site in a small caravan. Now that she's finished, she's intending to write a light-hearted account of her exploits.

☆   ☆   ☆   ☆   ☆

How did you have the idea first of all that you'd like to build your own house?

Rita: I was forty, I was on my own, my daughter had grown up. I was not working at the time. I'd always wanted to build a house. Lots and lots of people have wanted to, and it's a common ideal thing to do. And I thought "It's now or never".

A lot of things came together:

My own house – I could raise the cash if I sold it;

I'd no responsibilities family-wise;

I'd no job ahead of me, at least none that I particularly wanted; and I was a free agent.

I'd got thirty or forty more years of my life to fill up. You can't just sit on your bottom and be unemployed, or whatever, for the rest of thirty years, can you? It was the right time for me to do it. I knew I wasn't getting any younger. You either get on with it there and then, or it would be gone altogether.

So those are my basic reasons. It was a mixture of things really.

So how did you first get started?

Rita: Well, I would say that my career with my hands started when I was less than nine years old. I started with making things. I always made models. I made dolls' clothes, and I made my own clothes, and I did soft furnishings and I did a little woodwork to go with it; and progressed on from things like that. There was no specific time when I picked up my training; it had come from such a long way back – apparently unrelated things. But when you measure for a dress, and you have to think not to cut two left-hand sides when you want a left and a right, it's only the same as cutting architrave to go on the left and the right of a door frame. When I used to say to some of the builders "Oh, yes; it's like that in dressmaking", they'd think "What on earth is she talking about?". But the principles that you apply are taking care, and looking to see that you've got the pattern the right way round on each side, and that it matches. They are the same for so many things.

I can't really say that getting started was a very distinct moment for me. Though I suppose that when I borrowed eighty spare bricks from a neighbour and started bricklaying in my back garden, if any beginning was being made, it was then.

And how did you go on from there?

Rita: I began to deepen my studies, looking into books – not just generally how a house was built, but in detail; say, how the window reveals are, how the chimney is built, how brickwork dovetails with blockwork – the much finer details.

So you got a lot of books from the library?

Rita: Lots of books from the library, free books from the library.

The unfortunate thing in some ways is that Hornsea library is only a small library, and it caters particularly for little old ladies who like romantic novels. The only books in the building line are pretty well out of date. So this house is built very traditionally. In fact, when I was putting on my soffit bearers, attaching them to the ends of the rafters, one of the bricklayers came round, and he said "I haven't seen that done for years".

And I visited building sites. I became a little bit of a joke on the sites, in a good-hearted sort of way. The workmen were very helpful. I doubt if they would have been as helpful to a man; I think they would have seen him as a rival. I was a novelty, and I realized I was a novelty.

You were something to talk about in the pub?

Rita: That's right. And because of that, no doubt I was helped a lot more. In fact, people have said to me "How do find you get on with the workmen?". I say "Fine, if you approach them in the right way. You go to a workman and you want his help, so you say 'please', and you don't go in an overbearing way". Some men don't like to reveal their ignorance to a workman. To me, it doesn't matter a damn. The workmen think it's very funny.

The men were very good. I must have made thirty or forty site visits.

How long would you stand around on site talking to people?

Rita: If you've got a whole building site with, say, a dozen houses on it in various stages of construction, at the first house you might find a couple of bricklayers at work; so you might stand and watch them for ten minutes, and you might ask them a few questions while you're watching – admiring their handiwork! Next house, there might be a plumber at work. On one occasion I was watching a plumber and asking him questions, and he said "Here, have a go yourself". I had to say to myself "Come on, he'll stop me doing anything stupid, and he won't let me make a mess of the job". When I'd soldered my first three joints, I couldn't believe that I'd done it.

Sometimes, I'd just go and look at things when there was nobody there.

And on some sites you'd see how to do things wrongly?

Rita: Oh, yes. I saw a little bit of that as well.

So I did site visits, did lots of reading, and practised the bricklaying.

Then I had to look at legal work. Before you can sign a contract to sell your house and sign a contract to buy a piece of land, you've got to do a lot of work. You know that, once you've burnt your boats, you've burnt your boats. By the time I'd slowly worked my way through all the legal work and was getting very close to the point when I had to sign that document, I'd also learnt enough of the theoretical side of building. And I knew from my own experience of working with my hands that I had patience, I had a certain degree of skill in doing lots of different things.

Did you do any evening classes in woodwork or the like?

Rita: No.

You hadn't done anything practical in the building line before you started?

Rita: No.

I'd helped someone to put up coving once by holding it – I was the other pair of hands. That is pretty minimal. And I'd done lots of decorating. At that I needed no practice whatsoever.

With most of the work, I found that either it was boring or it was frightening. There is very little in-between time, when it is nice and pleasant and interesting.

First of all, it's frightening, like the plumbing was. There's an inbuilt fear in me. I always believe – I've always believed – that the other fellow has got the magic of how to do the job, and I haven't. Getting this stupid 'magic' idea out of my mind – it's been one of the biggest handicaps I've had.

There are certain things that many men don't do – it's woman's work. They don't get involved, they don't want to know how to even touch the job, let alone get started on it.

And women are like that with building work. With the plumbing, I was terrified of the blowlamp. I'd switch it on and off so quickly, as if it was going to bite me. I was so afraid of the blowlamp, I was shaking it, saying "Hurry up". The gas was getting shaken about and it was all coming out as yellow flames. It took quite a lot of enquiring around the sites to find why my joints weren't coming out as they should have done. As you know, yellow flames aren't hot enough. My fear made its own problem.

That's a little story that it's funny to look back on. But when you've got a copper joint that's just getting black with the carbon from the blowlamp, and the solder's not running, and you're biting your nails wondering what's going wrong – afterwards you can laugh about it, but not at the time.

I was saying about going round the sites. Another day, I was on a different site, and a chap was sawing up blocks, Celcon blocks. I watched him, and I said "That looks quite easy". He said "It is easy". So I said "Can I try?". So he said "Yes; you can cut me the next one". I was amazed how easily it cut. I couldn't believe that here was me, Rita, cutting a block up!

And not very long afterwards, somebody bought me a lump hammer and a bolster for looking after their kids for a few days. They said "What do you want for a present?". I said "I want a bolster!". I got a brick and I carefully marked it, and I cut it in two. I stood back in amazement.

So I began to count up. I could cut bricks in two, I'd soldered pipes, I'd sawn things in two. The things that I'd thought were very difficult to do, when I did them they weren't at all what I thought. But that's as I said, the woman and the woman's world being afraid of anything to do with the man's world.

When I first laid the bricks, it took me five days to summon up the courage to lay the first few bricks. Although I'd laid some in my back garden, I'd only used a 'practice mix' – mortar which doesn't set, so you can take the brickwork down afterwards. I had thought I'd get a bricklayer, although I'd done very well in my back garden. People said how neat my bricklaying was. It was quite tidy. Not the first time I did it! But by the time I'd done it eight times, I was getting pretty good at it.

What were you doing?

Rita: I put up a couple of corners and laid bricks to the line in between. And then it would take me a couple of hours to knock the walling down and clean up all the bricks.

When was this?

Rita: That was in the late summer of '84. By the autumn of '84, I'd built a house on paper, pretty thoroughly. I had a particular plot in mind, and designed to suit the plot. I was pretty deeply involved by then. Throughout '84, one of the things I was looking for was an excuse not to proceed with the project, a let-out. All the time, I was looking for the one nut that I couldn't crack, something that I couldn't do myself, or afford to pay to have it done.

I broke the house down into little bits, like:
   Doing the front doorstep. Yes; I could do the front door step
   Putting one window in – it doesn't matter about all the rest – just one window. Yes; I could put a window in.

When you break it down, you can do each little bit. I didn't really find a nut that I couldn't crack. Plastering I knew I'd have to pay for, unless I was going to be very brave.

When I got to the end of '84, I realized that I had no excuse. By that time I'd asked so many people questions, and they were all saying "When are you starting?". And I'd say "Well I have to think first". Word had got round that I was building a house, and I didn't dare back out.

It was a gradual decision. But when I eventually signed the contract for the land, that was one of the hardest moments that I've ever had. With the actual signing, you realize that you've committed yourself.

When was that?

Rita: That was December '84. By that time, I knew the enormity of what I was about to do.

Did you do your own conveyancing?

Rita: Yes – it's not too difficult once you get over some of the words the solicitors use. If I said that solicitors were thieving bastards, that would be about the size of my reckoning of them – but you can rub that off the tape. I agree that their work is probably useful, but I don't agree with the rate at which they're paid. My buying and selling cost me £50. That was for fees that you just can't avoid. I didn't find it too difficult.

I liked Bradshaw's book [*Bradshaw's Guide to DIY House Buying, Selling and Conveyancing*]. He says that when it comes to the difference between an amateur conveyancer and a professional, a keen amateur can beat a professional time after time after time. I would not pay for conveyancing again unless it was a really complicated case. The first time you do conveyancing, it's hard, but the second time is a lot easier.

When I had to sign that contract, I put it on my desk and it was there for quite a long time, two or three days. I kept going to look at it. When I signed it, there was this strange sense that this was the big thing, a sense which I've never quite had again since. As I say, I worried for five days before I laid a brick, but that was different somehow. And I didn't sleep the night before my first concrete lorry came.

Did you have an architect to design the bungalow?

Rita: No; I designed it myself.

But I knew that, when I come to sell it and somebody wants to have a mortgage to buy it, then they will have to have a piece of paper which is either NHBC, or an architects' certificate.

[Actually, with many building societies, a certificate is not necessary for a mortgage on a second-hand house.]

I did the drawings, and gave the architect the drawings; and he's been every now and again just to see what I've been doing and to look over the work.

Was the architect helpful in other respects?

Rita: Occasionally I asked him things – not very often because I had to go down to the town to ask him. Whereas, if there are chaps available on the site or I've got it in a book, I'll get the information like that much more quickly.

One of the things he did do for me, that I was very pleased to have done, was the levels. When I had my foundation pegs in, to get the levels he came along with a laser kind of instrument. He set it up, and went round touching each peg with a special stick. He told me that two of my levels were spot on, one was three millimetres too low, and the other was three millimetres too high. I didn't know at the time, but I realize now that was bloody good. I also realize that there is a certain amount of luck in that. I was only using a spirit level on a twelve-foot board. I suppose I got it right by doing it so many times to make sure.

Did you enjoy designing your home?

Rita: I enjoyed the designing a lot.

I had a funny way of doing it. Now we ladies have always done things in odd ways I've no doubt.

I stuck pins in my carpet. The pins marked the corners of scaled down rooms. I wrapped black cotton around the pins to represent the walls. And I used scaled, paper cut-outs to represent furniture in plan view. I used these cut-outs to test whether the proposed rooms were conveniently shaped and sized. If the 'rooms' couldn't accommodate the 'furniture' comfortably, the size of the room could be easily altered by shifting the pins and rewinding the cotton. When I'd arrived at the appropriate room sizes, I drew the finalized plan on paper in the normal way.

Rita Blooman's bungalow ~ nearly finished !

You went for a bungalow because—

Rita: —I've no head for heights! I was terrified on the scaffolding. I don't think that even having built this bungalow as a trial run that I would want to build a house. There's a lot of extra work in the staircase and all the other things that go with it. But basically, when it comes to the bricklaying up on that scaffolding, I'm frightened – though I did get used to it eventually. And maybe, if it was very good scaffolding, then I might manage a house.

When did you start to build?

Rita: April '85.
   I hand-dug the trenches.

Amazing! How long did that take?

Rita: About three weeks.

Was that to save money?

Rita: It was for a sort of odd reason. I'm a gardener for a start. So I was used to digging. But this land is pretty grim stuff, I can tell you. Builders said to me "You won't dig this land". So I tried one day, and thought "My God! They're right, it's terrible stuff". So I decided to have the excavator come. The ground was clay and hard as iron. The ground was so hard that I couldn't get the wooden pegs in for setting out. So I'd get a metal peg, and bang the metal peg in. And then I'd pull it out and bang the wooden peg in.
   A couple of days before the excavator was due, it started to rain. It rained solidly. The excavator driver excavated the back trench, and by the time he'd finished this his machine was in axle deep. He was looking very worried, and I was feeling very worried, and the rain was still throwing it down. I looked at him and said "What do you think?". He said "I don't like this". So we packed in at ten o'clock.
   I was heart-broken because I had the concrete gang booked for Saturday morning. I had no telephone on site, so I had to bike round: I had the building inspector to cancel, the architect to cancel, the concrete to cancel.
   After the excavator driver had gone and I'd gone to the phone in the town and phoned everybody up – or biked round – and said "It's all off", I got back to the site and I really felt awful. It's as though I was a big failure.
   So I had my lunch, and thought "What am I going to do? It could be a week before this land is dry enough for an excavator to work, longer if it rains again". So I thought "I can't sit in this caravan. There's an awkward trench to dig out by the garage. It will help if I dig that out. It's better than sitting in the caravan". So I started to dig that bit out. And it rained. And I dug a bit more. And it rained. And by the time it stopped raining, two weeks later, there was only one trench left to dig. So I thought "Well, what the hell, I may as well finish it".

So it was all due to the rain?

Rita: Yes; it was the bad weather. If it had brightened up the next day, I'd have rebooked the excavator and proceeded.

But it was so bad for so long. The trenches were flooded twelve times. I was for ever round the site borrowing pumps. There were two places where the trenches collapsed a little, but it could have been a lot worse.

The concrete was put in for the footings on June 3rd. I had a very easy time. The chap came on time; he bought us six cube metres of concrete the first delivery, and a cube and a half about two hours later. Me and Martin did most of the work, and a couple of others came and helped for the last half hour. The weather was very good.

Did you find that the concrete drivers all ask you if you want more water added?

Rita: Yes. "Do you want me to wet it up a bit?" is their usual question. And the more water that goes in, the weaker the mix becomes.

Did you use bricks or blocks for the foundation walls?

Rita: I used big blocks, 10″ by 12″, and 6″ deep.

You know the standard 9″ by 18″ block that people commonly use? They used to use two 'skins' in the foundations and then fill in the cavity with concrete. Well, I was going to do that. Then one day I came up here to a site and saw a local builder laying these 10″-by-12″-by-6″ blocks flat, in a single skin. I looked and watched, and thought "Well, that's easier to lay than a double skin, especially for someone who isn't so sure of their verticals". I found out what their price was, and it seemed to compare quite favourably. I thought "Those blocks are for me".

You can lay these blocks either way, to give you a 10″ or 12″ thickness of wall. With a 10″ thickness, the cavity walls would have been overhanging the foundation walls a little, so I preferred the 12″ thickness though it costs a little more.

I had the first lorry-load of oversite concrete on the second of August, and I'll never forget that day. The second batch came about ten days later.

What happened on the day you'll never forget?

Rita: Well, that day the first part of the oversite concrete was to be laid; I was due to have six cu. metres, a full load. I'd booked my people to come and help.

How many people?

Rita: I was supposed to have five, and myself. One was sick, one never appeared, one was on a bus that broke down. That left three of us. The lorry was a couple of hours late, so I was paying these two lads for nothing. When the concrete did arrive, it didn't take me very long to sus out that the two lads didn't know how to tamp properly – they couldn't co-ordinate their actions together. So eventually, I ran round to all the neighbours and said "Excuse me, I've got a load of concrete going off. Please can you come and help?". Now some of the neighbours were selfbuilders, and three chaps came. But the overall result was that the oversite concreting wasn't as good as I'd have liked it to have been. I had thought of having some insulation on top of the concrete and then just chipboard flooring. But I decided that the concrete wasn't good enough. Therefore I screeded the floor. But that day was a pretty horrendous day.

When I concreted the foundations, the chap came onto the site with his big concrete lorry. I remember standing by this huge lorry and thinking "God, if that thing rolls on me!". It rather overpowers you. It's not the sort of thing that one is used to dealing with. But by the time the lorry came to bring the oversite concrete – this was a month or two later – I was sufficiently adept with lorry drivers to get him to back up his lorry as needed and ask, Can you drop me that much there, and that much there. Whereas at first, they just used to drop the stuff where they found it convenient for themselves!

I was quite amused at myself. Just imagine a big, craggy lorry driver, who looks as though he spends his nights in the pub – not exactly a creature of finesse – and picture me saying "Do you think you can just shove your chute round there". At the time, I could see myself directing all this and not quite believing it. But at first, as I say, it was pretty frightening.

Did you lay the garage floor with the oversite?

Rita: I hadn't intended to, but the garage floor did get laid at the same time as the oversiting. The readymix man brought a bit too much concrete. He said "Well, I thought you might have underestimated". So I thought "You bloody liar, you'd never do that. There's some other reason". So we finished up with more concrete than we actually needed. So I said "Bung the spare in the garage". It bought the floor up to the 'finished' level instead of the sub-screed level that I'd intended. So I said to one of the chaps who'd come and helped me "Can you, by any chance, give it a good finish?". He said "Oh, you want a steel float finish on it. I've got my tools, I'll do it for you". And so I got it all done and finished.

The bricks below the dpc are a different colour. Are they special?

Rita: They are blue engineering bricks, and are swines to lay for an amateur. The reason is that they don't absorb any water at all. And the water in the mortar between them will just run down the face of the brick. But I read in an old book – one of the advantages of the old books is that they tell you the old tricks – and it said that the bricklayers used to have some dry-mixed sand-and-cement to hand whilst laying these bricks. Before they put the mortar down on the blue bricks, they sprinkled on the dry mix, like salt-and-peppering the brickwork with this dry mix. And then they put the mortar down, and put some more dry mix on top. And then they put the brick on it. The dry mix soaked up the excess water. You can really make a mess of those blue bricks when you're laying them.

And the blues are heavy, of course – no frogs or holes.

And that's the stage when you're a real novice.

Rita: Yes; you're starting there [below the dpc].

I laid the bricks in a very distinct order. I started with the south wall, which wouldn't be overlooked, and left the front wall till last.

Did you use a plastic dpc as well?

Rita: Yes. You don't have to, though, with engineering bricks below the dpc.

Did you use a dpc under the internal walls?

Rita: No. I ran the damp proof membrane over the whole site. Then one day when I was starting to put the internal blockwork up, one of the builders said to me "You've got to put some dpc under there, you know". And I said "Well, what for?". So I rang the building inspector, and I said "I don't want to put more damp-proofing under the internal walls, because it's unnecessarily putting a wall on a piece of plastic, and it can slither around". It didn't seem right. I said "After all, there's a dpm down below". And he agreed with me.

There's something I have to laugh about now, it was a bit silly: I made my house 52 bricks long and 38 bricks wide, exact numbers of bricks. And I realized afterwards that the only courses that were complete, all the way round the house, were the two courses over the lintels. It's not worth bothering about.

And all the internal walls are positioned so that they join the outside walls where block ends occur in the cavity wall. And the room widths and window positions are conditioned by a block ending. I wouldn't bother doing that again.

Rita, showing me some photos taken by the local newspaper: Here's a photo showing two inches of snow laying over the building. Notice the date, October 6th – as early as that. I was going to have a brickie come and help me in November, but because of the time lost through this bad weather, he had to make up on what he'd missed elsewhere. It kept on snowing and raining, and nothing got done. So eventually, I slowly put a course of bricks on, and then another course and another.

What a winter we had! There were times when the only thing I could do was to cut the blocks, ready for laying in the internal walls. I had all the blocks cut and numbered. There were times when that was all you could do; you couldn't lay the bricks because of the continual frosts.

Is it awkward being left-handed?

Rita: No, no. I'm told that brickies like to work in pairs, one left-hander and one right-hander.

I didn't have any scaffolding at all along the eaves walls. Instead, I had two wooden trestles, waist high. Every twelve bricks I laid, I had to move the trestles on. As the building went up, I put blocks underneath the trestles. That way I got all the low eaves walls done, and four courses up into the gables. Then I had my scaffolding just on the gable ends.

Where did you get your scaffolding from, because it's a bit of a problem for the selfbuilder?

Rita: Well, I knew if I bought scaffolding it would cost a lot of money, so wondered if I could make some wooden scaffolding and then use the wood inside the house later on. And I got a book on scaffolding, and here's an interesting fact: wooden scaffolding was used to put up the skyscrapers of New York. And I thought to myself "Well, what are you worrying about! Skyscrapers can be built from wooden scaffolding!".

But as it turned out, I didn't need to do any of that because one of the builders nearby had got his scaffolding down at just the time that I wanted to put mine up. So I said "Could I please borrow your scaffolding?". And he said "You pay me to put it up and take it down, and you can use it. It's better for me to have it up on a building than lying on the ground where it can be nicked". I knew him quite well – I knew all the builders quite well by this time. And so the scaffolding was put up for me, and three or four months later it was taken down again. It was very convenient for me. The builder who lent the scaffolding only built one house at a time, and he did all the work, him and his lad, so it obviously took him a long time to fit out a house – and during that time he didn't need his scaffolding.

But when I first went up on the scaffolding to work – of course, you've no wall in front of you. You've got to build that wall, haven't you? The fact that I could see the drop below me, I didn't like that at all. Inside my shoes, I could feel my feet clinging – as though my foot clinging to the shoe would save me from falling! I used to watch ladies walking by to the shops, and think "If only they knew the drama that was going on, up on this scaffolding!". I was terrified for quite a long time.

One day I was up on the roof trusses and I was having to nail some noggings [making up the gable ladder *in situ*]. And I had to lean out over an eight-foot drop. I had an eight-by-four [feet] sheet of old plywood that I'd found on the site, and I'd pulled it up onto the trusses to make a working platform. I was building up the inside leaf of the gable wall from the inside of the house. I could stand on this sheet, you see. But there was one point when I had to nail these noggings on, and I had to have both arms out, and I knew that drop was down below. It was only a 'bungalow drop', but it's hard concrete nevertheless, and it could still do you a nasty injury. I thought "I daren't do it". So eventually I got some rope and tied it around my waist, and I tied myself to one of the beams.

Like a mountaineer?

Rita: What I hadn't realized was that a neighbour was watching me, and he suddenly shouted up "Don't do it, Reet. Life's not that bad!". *Laughter.*

It was a bit of a joke – as somebody who had such a fear of heights, how did I come to build?

Once I went onto the top scaffolding of one of the houses round here, and they were just taking the scaffolding down, and I wanted to see one of the roof details. They'd taken the hand-rail off. And they'd taken a couple of the planks away – there were only three planks left. I looked down, and I couldn't move. This lad shouted up to me "You're scared, aren't you?". And I shouted back "I'm bloody terrified". I said "Never mind about the roof detail, I've had enough". And I couldn't get back on the ladder. Normally, I thought, the last thing you ever do is to actually touch a builder, but I said "Clive, Clive, just give me a hand". The builders thought that was really hilarious, they did. But I thought "What other person on a building site could stand at the top of a ladder and be terrified, and actually dare to shout back 'I'm bloody terrified'?". A man couldn't, could he? He'd never live it down.

But I eventually did get used to scaffolding to some degree.

Your fear of heights was the reason you had the tiling done?

Rita: One of the reasons.

The big reason was that the tilers gave me a very good offer. It was one of those 'cash, and we'll fit it in when we're rained off elsewhere' jobs. They said they'd do it for £120, including putting the felting on. If it had cost £1,000 – and everybody had said it would cost me £1,000 – then I'd have done it myself. But for £120, I reckoned I'd got a bargain.

Did you put the roof trusses on?

Rita: No; I made the orange juice that day.

Well, no, I had a bigger role than that. I did all the ordering of the materials. And I said to the chap who lent me the scaffolding "Will you put my roof trusses up for me? That's one thing I just can't do on my own".

When Harry and Clive were hauling the trusses into position, I had to help pull them across the building. When they started to stand the trusses upright, I had to steady them – that was my job. It's one of those things like a bike. So long as they're upright and in balance, there's no problem. But if they begin to topple, you've had it. So my job was just to keep the trusses balanced – and make the orange juice, and look pretty and ornamental, and that sort of thing.

Actually, it didn't work out too well. For the truss positions, I'd marked the wall plate at 600 mm centres, and when the builder, Harry, came along to put the trusses up, I said "Look, you'll see I've marked the wall plates very clearly. For the ends of each truss, I've marked a pair of lines, and the truss end fits between them". After six or seven trusses had been fixed, I happened to glance at the lines on the wallplate.

"Harry, you've let the trusses wander from their positions", I said.

"I can't have done", he answered.

"You're an inch or two adrift", I insisted. "The trusses should be at 600 mm centres."

"Oh! I was centering them at two feet", Harry responded.

So I said "Look, I'll tell you what we'll do, Harry. Continue with your blasted two feet until you get to the chimney. And beyond the chimney, we're going to change to the metric markings".

I'd marked the wallplate so plainly that you wouldn't have thought we could have got it wrong. But, you see, Harry was used to spacing trusses at two feet. And being an older tradesman and used to his feet and inches, he did two feet.

Did you put a gable ladder up?

Rita: No; I built the ladder *in situ.* I did actually order the ladders but they didn't come. Then I realized it was actually easier to build the ladders *in situ.*

When I came to put the barge boards up, and the fascia boards, I nailed a little loop of string to the ends of each board to hold the boards in their required positions: I hung them, like clothes on a washing line, from suitably positioned nails knocked into the roof rafters. By adjusting the size of the loops, all the boards were exactly positioned – in spite of being five metres long.

A lot of my problems have been like that – one person doing a job which needed two. Of course, I expected that.

There are some jobs which are much easier with two people.

Rita: Yes; they can be done by one, but it takes ten times as long. I just had to put up with that.

I was proud of finishing my chimney. I had a topping out ceremony, and put flowers in the chimney pot! [The decorated chimney pot is shown on the front cover. For the meaning of 'topping out', see the Glossary.]

What about the sealed units for the windows? Were they fitted for you?

Rita: Yes; that was bought as a 'job lot'. It cost me £650. That included some toughened glass. I had five quotes with a big variation in price.

One person I know has got condensation between the panes, but mine have been alright.

You had your roof on in August, '86. When did you have your glazing done?

Rita: About five weeks after the roof was done.

So it was weathertight for the winter?

Rita: It was weathertight. But despite it being weathertight, because there had never been any heating in it, there were times when I was working in it, and the temperature outside was minus-twelve and it was minus-five in the house. I got some strange marks on my legs. I didn't know what they were, so I went to the doctor. He said "Let's have a look". So I whipped my jeans down, and he looked at the marks and he laughed. I said "What's so funny?". He said "Two or three years ago, we didn't know what to make of it when we saw people turning up with marks like that on their legs. We've learnt that, with people who wear tight jeans, the air and the warmth can't circulate, and they get chilblains". I'd actually got chilblains on my legs, and I'd been working indoors.

Inside, you did the plasterboarding, but not the plastering?

Rita: No; I did neither. But I did order all the materials. I decided that I wanted metric plasterboards. So I asked the builders' merchant to get me some metric boards. This was five weeks in advance of when I wanted them. But five days after ordering the boards, the plasterers suddenly arrived at the front door and said "We've had a job cancelled. So we'd like to start on Monday".

So I started fitting the noggings [to nail the plasterboard to, in better quality work]. I'd got to do all round the edges of the house, and all the middle ones at 1.2 metre spacings. There was 120 noggings to go in. Then the man from Jewson's turns up and says "We can't get you the metric boards". I said, "Please, get me them somehow". And he said "No; there is just no way". I begged and pleaded with him. I said "Look, I've fitted all my bloody noggings for this spacing". Eventually, I realized there was no way I was going to get these metric boards. So I took the noggings down and repositioned them to suit imperial boards.

The plasterboard was due to be delivered on the Friday; the plasterers were due to turn up on the following Monday. It didn't come on Friday, it came on Monday morning. And when it came, it was metric!

Was it really?

Rita: I had to take all the bloody noggings back out, with the plasterers hammering at me, saying "Come on, Reet!".

Did you swear?

Rita: I got on that blower to Jewson's – I had to go to my neighbour's house. I let rip at that bloke on the phone like I have never let rip at anybody else.

One thing that had really got me was when I checked with the driver and said "Look, bloody metric". He said "We've always had them". I said "Always? I've been told it takes three weeks to get them". He said "We haven't had eight-by-fours [feet] for years"!

Another annoying thing I found was when I bought a window board and it was meant to fit into the groove in the window frame. They have a tongue and you expect the tongue to fit into the groove. Mine didn't. I had to borrow an electric planer and shave a bit off. I've had quite a few things like that, where things are made to fit and, when you actually get them, they do not. I find that extremely annoying.

How did you fix the window boards down?

Rita: I mortared into the brickwork some pads, and then I nailed into these. I like all-white paintwork which covers over the nails. [A window board needs to be fixed down to the wall beneath it. A common method it to insert wooden pads between the bricks or blocks and to nail through the board into the pads.] I'd done one or two when I realized that I was nailing into end grain, and I thought "No, that's no good". [That is, the grain of the pads was orientated vertically instead of horizontally.]

With the builders, all you see is a rough lump of wood rammed down, like a big chip for the fire. It's end grain, but there's no pull in that end grain. I suppose they tend to go on doing what they've always done. Whereas, I read a book and see what you're supposed to do.

I did have one funny thing by reading a book. One of the builders' merchants said "You haven't half thrown a cat amongst the pigeons". What happened is that I ordered my lintels, and I ordered them from the Catnic book. But the man at Jewson's said "What do you want CN43's for? Everybody else had CN8's". So I said "Well, that's what the Catnic people say you want for these 5″ blocks". "Well, nobody else has them". Eventually they rang Catnic, who said that it was perfectly right, with a 5″ block you should use CN 43's.

All the brickies, when they'd gone from 4″ to 5″ blocks, just used the same old lintel as they'd always used. The man at Jewson's said "Suddenly, we've got to start ordering CN43's because of you, Madam".

I think there's an awful lot of that in many trades, that people go on doing what they've always done, even though it doesn't really apply any more.

What blocks are they then, these 5″ blocks?

Rita: They're Celcon Turbo blocks. You can get 6″ ones now for an even better standard of insulation.

Unfortunately for me, in all the time I was on building sites, asking many, many questions – I used to ask thousands of questions – nobody ever thought to say to me "By the way, some blocks split".

The inner leaf of my outside wall has a crack down it in two places.

What was the cause of the splitting?

Rita: I'm not sure. It happened at the time when it was extremely cold. It wasn't due to them being wet, they were perfectly dry. There was a big temperature drop, and the blocks contracted.

When did you finish the house? When did you get a completion certificate?

Rita: I sent in my card that said I was fit for occupation just before Christmas, 1988. I said that it's not complete, I haven't finished all the trim, but it's finished as far as the building inspection is concerned. I officially moved in just before Christmas.

I had to have it for Christmas. My daughter was coming, and we'd waited a long time. The Christmas of 1984 was the last Christmas that we'd had at home, and we said "Here's to Christmas 1986". Well, in fact it was Christmas 1988. *Laughter.*

And now you're claiming your VAT?

Rita: I sent that in a couple of months ago. They sent me an odd query or two back, and said that you're not allowed to claim on gas hobs any more, and the like. Every time they send me a query, I send them another batch of bills, because I've still got to finish.

What a business it is, filling those forms in! They wanted to know how many litres of paint you've used, how many cubic metres of joinery!

How did you find living in your little caravan?

Rita: Not bad, because I had an electric fan heater and that kept it dry and sufficiently warm. The coldest temperature I recorded was $-12°C$. The Calor gas froze up, my washing froze in a bucket, and all the washing up froze together. Despite all that, I didn't do too badly, mainly because of the electric. I would certainly recommend anybody who was going to live in a caravan in winter-time to have electric fan heaters. Condensation was the big enemy; it was an utter crime to me to let the kettle steam. Occasionally the tap froze up. During the very cold weather, I used to clip an electric lamp by the tap overnight. In February '85, it was on day and night to keep the water from freezing up.

Did you get Planning Permission for your caravan?

Rita: When I applied, somebody did object. Why, I don't really know. Some Councils grant it almost automatically. Others don't. [And some Councils concede that selfbuilders are construction workers, and so don't need Planning Permission to live on site.] I asked about it before I bought the plot, and the Planning officer said "Let me put it like this.

We've had a hundred cases through and a hundred cases have been passed". He said "I can only tell you what the Council has done. I can't tell you what they will do in your case".

So there was no great difficulty. But I made a great point, and always have done, of keeping the site tidy. The last thing I want is for people to say "Oh, it's like a gypsies' site". I thought "Yes; I am living in a caravan on the site, and people may not like it – it's a kind of a posh sort of area – but at least it'll be clean and tidy". I had some funny comments. One of the builders' merchants said "I've never had to wipe my feet to come on a building site before, Rita". *Laughter.*

An NHBC inspector one day said to me "You should belong to the NHBC – they give a prize for the tidiest site, you know". He was coming around inspecting one or two of the other sites, and I'd known him for some time. So when I saw his car come, if I needed to ask anything, I'd go and collar him; but he didn't mind. If I'd been a man, I'm sure that he'd have said to me "Look, if you want my information, you'd better join and pay your money".

What about the Local Authority building inspector? Was he helpful?

Rita: Very good.

Before I made a final design for the house, I showed my drawings to the building inspector and asked if he could find anything outstandingly wrong with it. He found one point: I had some windows a bit close to a corner of the house.

I designed my house to the Regulations, if you see what I mean – not the other way round. And then I went to see him to check it out. And when I submitted the plans, they passed through in due course without any problems.

When it came to the site visits, the local chap was super. Now some of the building lads don't like the building inspectors; it tends to be 'them and us'. But I would ask him because I wanted to know something. Some of the building lads were a right bit cocky with them, and of course, the inspectors don't like that. But I found that, if you treated them reasonably, they were very good. I've heard cases where they took their jackets off and actually helped.

Did you make any bad mistakes?

Rita: No; I didn't. And the reason I didn't was that I couldn't afford to.

Where I've made little mistakes it's usually due to changing the plan from the initial design. Where I've made errors, it's been the result of changing my mind. I did the original plan very thoroughly.

When I've made a change of plan, I've thought of maybe four or five things it would affect. But when I made the original plan, I'd maybe thought of ten things it would affect.

You had enough money yourself to build the whole place without a loan?

Rita: Yes.

The idea financially was that I sold my house and all the contents. I got £26,000 which was a good rate at the time. I already had £4,500 which I'd saved up. So I had about £31,000.

I spent £200 on my shed, I spent £9,500 on the land. The caravan was given to me – I eventually sent them £50 for a Christmas present. I reckoned that when I actually started building I had £20,000 plus the money it would earn in interest if I spent my money judiciously. I reckoned that the materials would cost me £10,000 to £12,000 at the time, and I allowed about £5,000 for labour. When it actually came to it, I didn't know whether I would be able to lay bricks. In actual fact, on the labour side, the plasterers were £500, the tilers £150, the plumber for the gas fitting £100. (The double glazing came as a job lot, so you don't know really what the labour charges are there.) And I had £80 to pay for a day's work on the roof trusses.

Wasn't that rather expensive?

Rita: It was for two men, and I suppose they were a day and a quarter. To me it was a problem solved.

Altogether, it was less than a thousand pounds. When I get my VAT money back, I'll have about £9,500 left.

I've lived for four years, but very frugally; I don't bother about clothes very much; I can make my own clothes if I need them – and on a building site you don't want them anyway.

I've scrounged things, I've been given them. Once I was baby sitting, and the chap said "I've got a hundred engineering bricks: £25, Reet?".
"Done."

Six months later, he gave me the cheque back; he never cashed it. He said "You're always baby sitting for us".

Because I had electric onto my site, quite a few of the builders said "If we bring a long cable, can we plug it in?". It was very handy for them. And I could say to them "When I'm concreting, could I borrow your men for half an hour?".

You'd bought an electric mixer. Did you have many other tools?

Rita: When I started off, I had to buy a barrow; I had the bolster and chisel that someone bought me as a pressie; somebody gave me a bricklayers' trowel – a cheap, horrible one; I had a few screwdrivers, gardening tools – I've broken four spade handles on this site; that shows the kind of land it is – and I had a few rusty odds and ends.

First time I was married, and then I lived with somebody for nine years. When we parted company, the scratty ends of his tools got left in a box in the garage, and I thought they might come in handy. I bought a five-metre tape measure. I had a claw hammer, I had a hand drill, I had a couple of panel saws, not much more. I'd bought a level. My entire collection of tools could have been fitted in a ladies' handbag, plus the saws and level. I knew I would have to buy a few odd things.

One of the things I was quite helped by was that, one day, this old chap poked his head over the top of the wall and said "Hallo. I've read about you in my newspaper". He looked round and said "By, aren't you neat!". And then he said "Haven't you got a trestle to work off? I'll make you a couple of trestles". I thought "I'll bet!". But two days later, round he came with these two trestles. I was quite impressed. He was a great help to me. He would sharpen the tools. But on the other hand, by as much time as he saved me by sharpening the tools, he wasted by chattering to me.

Did you have any accidents at all?

Rita: Touch wood; no.

One day I fell off a milk crate. I was stepping on to it, and the ground gave way, and it tipped me over on my back. I've had slight back trouble for many years – I put it down to gardening. So long as I'm moving about, it doesn't bother me. Therefore I felt my back was a little bit at risk. I was quite surprised when, two minutes later, I picked myself up and dusted myself down.

I am very accident conscious.

It's like: if you've got no money and you can't afford to waste it, you don't. I couldn't afford to have an accident.

Did you take out any insurance? Did you insure the building or yourself?

Rita: I didn't insure the building until it was closed in, the glass was in. I didn't feel like paying £60 to insure a hole in the ground.

The other thing that I was aware of was that, if children came onto the site and there was any chance of me being sued for negligence, I would have to be able to prove that there was no negligence. So when I made stacks of blocks or bricks, I stacked them in pyramids because, if kids climbed on them, there was less risk of a lot coming down. The best insurance was to make sure that there could be no negligence.

I've never believed in insurance to a great degree. The only insurance I have is on the house, and it's for the building. All the furniture I buy is second-hand. I can replace the entire lot for a couple of hundred quid. A lot of it is fitted furniture anyway, insured as part of the house: the bathroom, the kitchen, the wardrobes. All the furniture in my last house was either made myself, or bought second-hand and done up. I like to think that, when I've done the furniture, you wouldn't know that it hadn't just come out of a shop.

I did ask about personal insurance, but they wanted to treat me as if I were a full building worker. [Modestly priced insurances for self-builders are now available.]

The other thing I'm very careful of, if I'm doing a job that requires a lot of tools: I'll clear the ground before I start work. Now lots of workmen – the rubbish they work amongst! You step back and you're treading on your drill. Men seem particularly partial to that. I like it cleared because I think that if I step back and I hurt myself – that's me finished. And I just don't like to be hurt.

Are you more confident of your skills now?

Rita: Yes; but there are quite a few times when just a little bit of me has done a job and doesn't quite believe that I've done it. I find that rather nice. If I ever lose that, I will be sorry. Seeing a rainbow through a child's eyes, or pantomime, is something rather special. And just occasionally, I look at things and just a little bit of me doesn't believe that I've done it.

That's one of the things that, when people know me well enough, they're surprised at: how little confidence, in some ways, I have. It took me five days to lay a brick. I have this mechanism inside me:

I fear on one hand. And on the other hand, I have an impatience with myself. And I'll build up to a state of six of fear to five of impatience; but eventually I have six of impatience to five of fear – and then I move.

If ever there's a big job, it doesn't usually take me as long as five days; but often, for two days I will twitter about. I will be doing what I call 'legitimately putting it off': the washing's got to be done, the caravan's got to be cleaned, better do the shopping, or sometimes even building things. I don't have somebody saying to me "When are you going to get that done?". It's just got to come from within yourself.

I've often met people who really couldn't even put a screw in, and yet they'd have more confidence about lashing into a new job. And they're surprised when I hesitate. They say "You've done all this. Why are you worrying about putting tiles on?". I say "Well, I've never tiled before".

Did you ever get dispirited about how long the work was taking you?

Rita: Not really; no. I think to a certain degree I knew that once I'd burnt my boats and signed that piece of paper that bought me this land then I was stuck with it. I just had to make it work.

I was also very keen that every job I did, I got it right. I couldn't afford to get it wrong; I couldn't afford to just scrap a load of materials. So I would do a practice run first. Like my letterbox:

I'd never cut a hole in an expensive door. So I got a plank that was the same thickness as the door, and I cut my letterbox. I went round showing everybody – "Look at my letterbox in the plank!".

A lot of the jobs, therefore, I did twice, because I had to do a practice run and then one to do it.

Putting all the handles on the doors, I would see how straight I could use a brace and bit. Some bits keep themselves centred but mine didn't – it was only a spade bit. I arranged this wonderful system of mirrors. I put a big rubber band round the door and I attached a carpenters' square to the door. And I put a mirror across the door, and I could see if the bit was level. If you're looking down you can't see that. But it all had to be rigged up.

The day when I really felt worse was that day I mentioned: when the excavating and the concreting had to be cancelled; and it was such a hassle just to cancel it; and the fact of sitting in my caravan and wondering how long it was going to go on raining for. And that was right at the start – the first thing you do is peg out and excavate. The first thing I'd done was up the creek.

The oversiting was a bad day too?

Rita: That was from the sheer trauma of the day; yes. If you get a pile of concrete that sets you've got a big problem, an expensive problem. That wasn't a disappointment so much as anxiety. There's a slight difference, isn't there? I was just angry in some ways.

Whereas the other one was more despair. Of course, it was in winter, the weather was awful, nothing to cheer you on at all. But I realized that I could either sit in the caravan and be miserable and be cold, or I could get out there with my shovel and at least do something and not be spending money on heat. That was, I think, the closest to despair I ever had, right at the start.

But having spent a year, nearly, doing all the preparation in my head, that didn't leave an awful lot of surprises. I think that's a good thing.

But as I say, with most things I do, I practise.

And I look for a good method.

For example, when I was doing the tiling of the back door step, I knew I didn't have this particularly well. What I did was to concrete the step, and I was trying to put the vertical and horizontal tiles on at the same time. It didn't quite work as well as it might have done. So I was talking to be builder about tiling and I asked him about it. He said "What we do, we put a plank in position, we slide the tiles in behind the plank, and then we pack behind the tiles with the mortar. So you know the tiles will be straight to the board and all come to the top of the board". (You can actually get adhesive and stick them on, but I didn't know that. I only knew the old-fashioned method.)

So I thought "That's a foolproof method". But of course, you do have to build an elaborate formwork for it, to make sure it's all square and as you want. But at least, if you do the woodwork wrong, you can always take it to bits and have another go.

What part of the building did you enjoy the most?

Rita: Of all the tasks, probably joinery, the finer points of the joinery. I won't say I enjoyed it, but I found it the least worrying.

The aspects that I found the most worrying to me were the brickwork, getting it straight – terrified that, if it was wrong, I'd have to do wonders with woodwork to make it look right. But I wasn't capable at that stage of doing wonders with woodwork.

And the plumbing I found worrying. I don't think that if I did the plumbing again that I'd find it as worrying.

Is that because of the blowlamp?

Rita: Yes. And I tried to do things that I wouldn't do again. I would cut all the lengths of pipe up for each room and then connect it up. But it may be two millimetres out at a joint and by the time you've got to the forth or fifth joint, it's not going to meet at all. So now, I'd do a bit and solder, do a bit and solder, so that you get rid of each error.

And I possibly wanted to do things that plumbers don't bother about usually. I wanted all the pipework to drain properly. So I wanted it all to run to falls. I didn't have much to work with, only about an inch. It was a bit tricky.

The plumbing and the brickwork I found difficult. But the second time around, it would be probably less so.

There were hairy bits as well: getting the fascias up into position, and the barge boards.

That was because you were on your own?

Rita: Because you're on your own.

Do you think that, as a woman, you found it more difficult than a man? Think of those cement bags!

Rita: There have been times . . .

For instance, I was taking the electrics out of my shed a week ago, and there was one screw I could not shift. I couldn't get this last screw out, and it was halting the whole job. I could even feel that, when I struggled at it, the muscles down through my stomach were pulling hard; it was hurting.

So I borrowed the young lad from across the road, about seventeen or eighteen – he hadn't come into his manly strength, as it were. I gave him the big screwdriver and pointed him at the screw. Yes, he bunched his muscles for a bit, but it was out in less than thirty seconds. Now I could bunch my muscles all day, and it would still be there. So there have been times when it was more difficult for me.

The highest feat of strength that I ever displayed was one day when the local builders' merchant turned up with ten bags of cement for me. Now, the lorry driver had hurt his shoulder. So he rolled the cement to the back of the waggon and very slowly let it down onto my arms so that I could cuddle it to my body; and I staggered into the house with it. I would think twice about that now because it is not very good for a woman to be carrying bags of cement. There are certain muscles it doesn't do any good for.

Would you recommend selfbuild to other people, to other women?

Rita: I'd recommend it to anyone who had the right attitude.

I don't think strength particularly comes into it. Are you the kind of person who can picture what you want, and be determined to go on gnawing away at that problem until you've found a solution? Really, I think you need somebody who's pretty dogged.

If you're prepared to do that, yes, I'd recommend it. I've never regretted doing it. I've regretted the weather was so awful sometimes, but what can you do about that? I wrote in my diary one day – and you must bear in mind that I'd been a non-believer, religion-wise, since the age of ten – I put "The weather is so awful I'm thinking of turning religious". From anybody else, that might not mean a lot, but anybody who knew me, they'd say "My God! It must have been terrible!". *Laughter.*

Yes; I'd recommend it to someone who had the right attitude . . .

Like perseverance?

Rita: Yes; perseverance. It's no good if you're the kind of person who the first time something goes wrong you want to give up and run away. When you've no alternative, you can't run away, can you?

Your achievements have been reported in the newspapers, and you've been interviewed on local radio. Have you enjoyed the media being interested in you?

Rita: Yes; it was a bit of fun – rather like you coming today.

I had a lady reporter come one day, and she indicated the mortar I was laying the bricks with, and she said "And how do you get on mixing the concrete?". I said "My dear, it's not concrete". How could somebody be so basic as not to know the difference between cement, concrete and mortar? But then, if you asked most women what was the difference, a lot of them would have difficulty – and quite a few blokes as well!

Have you got any plans for building another one?

Rita: That depends. If I sell my book, and make a bomb out of it – which as you know is highly unlikely – I shall sit back and enjoy it. If there was a really cushy teaching job going – a nice little junior school – I would take it. But if I had to go and teach at a school like I taught in at Leicester, which was a rough school at the back end of Leicester. . . I taught there for four months, and all I did virtually was just count off the days. I didn't like spending my time persuading kids who really didn't want to work, to get on with something. They just wanted to be as stupid and as silly as they could, and I didn't have much time for that – being a diplomat, trying to get them to work. At junior school, you say "Do it". But you can't do that with the senior school. And they know you can't, and they take advantage.

Now if I was offered that job again or build another house – and start in the mud, with the caravan – I'd say "Just give me the mud and the caravan". I can honestly say that building, compared to teaching in a rough school, is a doddle.

GEORGE
READ

A HOUSE IN FOUR MONTHS

BUILDING YOUR OWN HOUSE doesn't have to take years – it can be done in months. George Read built a three-bedroomed house in less than four months. Needless to say, for such a rapid construction, the timber-frame method was used, and all the work was subcontracted. With the plinth in place, it took only a few days to put up the frame, and the house was completed totally within a further three months – and finished luxuriously at that, with gold-plated taps, a specially commissioned onyx fireplace to match the carpet, decoratively moulded covings, walls papered throughout (with matching bedspreads in the bedrooms), and so on.

Yet George Read had had no previous building experience. He is, however, in the Territorial Army, so he called upon his experience there to plan the construction process like a military operation. The speed with which the house was built shows the success of this approach.

The house has a nominal floor area of about 130 square metres. It is accompanied by a vast double garage, for which George Read sees other uses in the future. They are built on an infill plot along a country road in Worcestershire. We began our conversation by talking about the plot.

☆   ☆   ☆   ☆   ☆

When did you buy this plot of land?

George Read: It came up for auction in February, 1987.

So you had to buy it at auction? That's a difficult situation.

George Read: Plots of land are few and far between in Worcestershire. I went to two auctions prior to that.

Originally, I approached the farmer up the road about land. There are two new houses now just up the road; that land was part of the farmer's field. I approached him and said "Have you ever considered applying for Planning Permission for this bit of land?". He said "No; not really". Anyway, to cut a long story short, he promised to sell it to me if he got Planning Permission. And then he didn't, he put it up for auction.

It went for £62,000, that plot did, and they got two houses on it. That was way, way above what I wanted to spend.

I went to the auction for this plot determined to get it, and we got it for £33,000.

So you had to have £33,000 to put down. How did you finance that?

George Read: We were lucky and unlucky: we'd sold our old house to the Council by compulsory purchase.

For a reasonable price?

George Read: We lost about £15,000. They agreed to buy it in the October. We didn't get the money until the April, and that was the time when house prices were escalating. So we lost the inflationary figure, plus the mortgage repayments.

But we got the money for that house, and that financed the buying of this land. Then we rented the house off the Council.

So you stayed in the house?

George Read: Yes. We were fairly fortunate in that respect. We were going to rent a house anyway, and build this at the same time.

As we were renting, we had to get it done fairly rapidly because every week we stayed in the house cost us £100 in rent.

That was an incentive to build quickly?

George Read: Oh, yes. I could have saved money by doing more jobs myself, or getting friends to do the jobs. But it turned out quite well at the end of the day.

I originally wanted a Georgian type house, but the Planning people suggested something with hip roofs and cottage style.

Is that what they preferred?

George Read: Yes. While I'm saying that, I'm very pleased with it.

So you looked round for a design in that style?

George Read: Yes; I looked through the selfbuild magazines and those sort of things – the different package deals you can have with various companies.

And you'd decided that you wanted to go for timber-frame?

George Read: Oh, yes; after I'd gone into it – originally, it was the brick-and-block.

What changed your mind?

George Read: The way it all came about really was I was talking to a chappie, a bricklayer, and he suggested that we get a 'trad pack' (that 'Purpose Built' supplied). A 'trad pack' includes all the timber and doors for fitting inside a traditional shell. We saw the designs for all their houses, and we finished up with one of their timber-frame ones.

Purpose Built were local, and they had the design which looked nice.

George Read's timber-framed house

Could you change the design at all to suit your particular requirements?

George Read: Oh, yes; we did. We amended it slightly - not that much because it would have meant more work for Purpose Built. And again, it was a matter of time.

How long did it take you to build the house?

George Read: I forget how long the Planning Permission took – that was a pain in the arse, to be honest, with the Planning people. As the plans were going through to be passed, we were under Wichhaven, and then we changed and went under Worcester. It was a right pain in the bum, really.

The footings were finished the first week in June. Then everything stopped because Purpose Built couldn't deliver the frame on time. So nothing happened for three weeks or so.

To be fair to them, how long previously had you ordered the package?

George Read: Oh, it wasn't long. It was in March or February. They were quite good. It's not too bad when you're talking about a house – it's a lot of timber.

How long did you take to do the foundations?

George Read: I had that done by a company in three weeks. Again, I would have done that myself. If I were to do this again, certainly I'd do the footings myself.

You virtually subcontracted all of this one?

George Read: All the lot.

I did all the ordering.

The managerial side?

George Read: Yes; the co-ordination.

What about the decorating?

George Read: I did the painting inside and out. That in itself is a job and a half. And did the tidying up.

Father-in-law did all the wall papering. Tradesmen did the rest.

We had good fun while it was being built. We had a bit of a giggle, a bit of a laugh. I'm saying that, but it was hard pressure, particularly as I'm not used to doing manual work.

I disappeared on TA camp on the fourth of July; the frame was delivered on the sixth; I came back after a week, and the frame was up.

We moved in at the end of September. The house was complete. We've done nothing since we moved in; even the garden was finished.

So you even had some garden contractors?

George Read: Yes; knowing full well that if I hadn't got the garden done, it would still be the same as it was.

It was a lot of bloody hard work, a lot of hard work, a lot of bother – frustrating, because you had to keep pressurizing the contractors. I had to pressurize the electrician to get the cable in before the plasterboard guys came in. Even then, I had to get onto the plastering team to postpone it for a week because the electrician hadn't finished.

But saying that, I planned it like a military operation, and then put pressure on people to turn up on time.

And you had the sort of job where you could take time out to organize things?

George Read: Oh, yes. I'm self-employed – I'm in sales. Of course, in sales you can do a day's work in a morning if you put yourself out. So every afternoon I was here, and every weekend. I was here from two o'clock to ten o'clock every night, seven days a week, doing basic labouring jobs and making sure that the tradesmen did their work. Just me being here made them a bit more particular. Even though they knew I didn't know a great lot about the building trade, just me being here made the difference.

Had you had any building experience, in fact?

George Read: No; none at all.

I just planned it out logically – just a bit of man-management and just a bit of organization; that was all basically.

So how did you finance it?

George Read: We had the money from the other house; and we borrowed the rest from the bank and then took out a pension mortgage afterwards.

And was the mortgage fixed up after you built it?

George Read: Yes; but the bank agreed it all beforehand. I'm in business with the bank.

So it's a mortgage with a bank?

George Read: Yes. I converted the loan to a pension mortgage afterwards. I could have got it from a building society, but it was easier to go to the bank.

Did they require an architects' certificate?

George Read: Yes. The architect used to come up and have a look at it, and just disappear.

He wasn't involved with the design, was he, because that was from Purpose Built?

George Read: No; he was just making sure that it was built as per the Building Regs basically, and built correctly.

Did you have trade accounts at the builders' merchants?

George Read: Yes.

It's surprising the bargains you can get if you shop around. Just on the insulation alone, I saved £7 a roll. On a timber-frame house, all the external walls have got to be insulated. And I insulated the internal walls as well, just to sound proof them – where normally you wouldn't bother, of course.

What did you put in there?

George Read: The same stuff, 80 mm, just to dampen the noise down in between the rooms. £7 a roll – it's surprising how you can save. I did that with everything, with the bricks, the roofing tiles . . . .

Do you remember how much the Purpose Built package cost?

George Read: Excluding VAT, it was about £11,000.

How much did they supply?

George Read: Every bit of timber. All the timber, with the exception of the patio door. And the door furniture.

Not the sealed units?

George Read: No.

You've had no trouble with the sealed units?

George Read: No; not yet.

In fact, there's been no trouble at all with the place yet. By supervising every single phase of the house – the amount of concrete that went into the footings was bloody unbelievable really – you know exactly what's there and what's happened.

How did you get on with the building inspectors?

George Read: OK. The inspectors were fine. It was the Planning people that were a pain in the bum. I took eighteen bricks down there. Every one was "Oh, no; I don't think that'll go". I was getting a bit peeved. I was going to tell him what I thought of him.

Were they fussy about the tiles?

George Read: They wanted the small, plain tiles; they wouldn't have the large ones.

They're concrete, but they're quite nice.

Are there any special features about the house?

George Read: It's very well fitted out inside. We didn't skimp on it.

The fencing was a costly item. It shocked me. The fencing alone was £1,200 – it was on both sides, you see. It's things like that that tot up.

I built the monster garage with a view to turning it into a bungalow. It's built to house specifications. There's insulation in the walls, there's water in there, electric in there, the lot in there. So if ever we come to move, I can try and get permission to turn that into a granny flat. All I've got to do then is to put in the windows and internal walls, take these garage doors out, skim it inside – and you've got a bungalow.

That was the plan for the future, in case we leave.

You didn't make any major mistakes while you were doing it?

George Read: No; everything went fairly smooth – no major boo-boos. And we've had nobody back to do anything. The only thing we have had is a leak in the front room, where it's been leaking through the shower tray. That's the only trouble, just one little leak.

Any accidents?

George Read: No.

If you were doing it again, would you do it any differently?

George Read: I'd do it slower, I'd do it a lot slower. I was absolutely 'tatered' at the end of it, to be honest. Shattered, I really was.

Did your wife get involved?

George Read: No; she didn't. She didn't really want to move. She didn't want to get too involved. On saying that, she does a lot for my business. But the father-in-law did a bit.

Is she happy enough now?

George Read: Oh, yes.

And you might build another one?

George Read: I'd personally like to do it again. My wife's not very happy about it, but I'd like to do it again – oh, yes – and take my time next time, and not try and rush things.

Why isn't your wife so happy about it?

George Read: Oh, she's happy here; she loves it here.

She doesn't want to move again?

George Read: That's what it is. She doesn't like the upheaval and the bother. The wife's the sort of person that, if the house needs decorating, it's got to be done in a day and have no mess. Which you can't do, of course.

Maybe not a package next time. I'd like to design my own place next, and have a say in what shape the rooms are and the rest of it.

So you're pleased you've done a selfbuild?

George Read: Certainly. I'd recommend people to do it. Though it's a worry, if you're that type of person. Nothing really bothers me to be honest; I don't get that excited.

You have to plan it out, and make sure it happens. But if you don't plan it out and you take people at their word, it can be a bother.

It's a matter of being positive. You've got to take a positive attitude. The father-in-law thought I was bloody stupid to be honest.

Does he still think that?

George Read: No, no; not now. He's changed his mind now.

It's just taking a positive step. It's a thing I've always wanted to do, and I've done it.

I'd recommend anyone to do it.

You would?

George Read: Oh, yes – because of the money you save.

Have you worked out the finances?

George Read: Yes. In total, it cost about £92,000. That's as it is. (The land was £33,000.) That's the lot, including the wall paper, the carpets, the fixtures and fittings, all new bed covers – everything matches. If you take off the luxuries to sell it in the state that a builder would sell it at, I'd have done it for about £18,000 less.

£18,000 less? That's a lot less!

George Read: There's a lot of expensive fixtures and fittings in there. A builder wouldn't have gone for gold-plated taps, he'd have gone for chrome taps, you know. And there's moulded coving and stuff like that. All the extras tot up. I mean, the garage is monstrous. That you wouldn't have. It would be a double garage, rather than really a quadruple. The garage is 30' by 18', something like that.

What do you think the value of the property was when it was built?

George Read: The two up the road which have virtually the same living area – though we have a bigger garage – they went for £135,000 at that time. So you save yourself quite a few pounds.

JOHN
SEYMOUR

AN ACRE IN WALES

TO INTRODUCE John Seymour's house, here is the introduction that he himself wrote for the sale particulars when he came to sell the house:

I'd like to take this opportunity to put you in the picture and tell you a little of the personal story of the creation of this unique house. Firstly you should know that this represents the realization of a dream for me. Eight years ago, I started looking for the kind of setting I wanted. After a year combing mid-Wales and on the point of giving up hope, I was amazed and delighted to find what I had been repeatedly told did not exist: an acre of secluded rural woodland with Planning Permission to build a house.

The dream was to design and build a charming home, blending the best of traditional and modern practice. I wanted to master all the skills involved. These detailed particulars are both for my own intellectual satisfaction, serving as a record of my achievement, and to inspire maybe those who appreciate the value of dreams come true.

The house itself is of simple rectangular plan. The outside walls have been uniquely rendered to look like stonework, and painted red. (In fact, the walls are composed of two leaves of blockwork, with the cavity partially filled with insulation.) The steeply pitched roof, with traditional rafters covered in slates, allows a large studio in the loft space. The nominal floor area is 120 square metres.

There is a separate double garage, of unusual construction, with a workroom above. Like the house, this building is very well insulated.

This story illustrates the need to be sure that you can finance a selfbuild right through to its completion.

☆   ☆   ☆   ☆   ☆

Is the house built of stone?

John: No; it's cavity wall of concrete blocks, with $1^{1}/_{2}''$ polystyrene insulation in the $3''$ cavity. But it's stone-effect rendered to make it look like a stone house.

It's a funny mixture. It was designed to look fairly traditional and be fairly simple, but also to be very well insulated, energy effective.

The garage and workshop is different. This is timber-frame with polystyrene rendered inside and out. So that's actually a very interesting building structurally.

When did you build this?

John: I started this in '76 and finished it in '84 – about eight years altogether, a long time. We ran out of money; the relationship broke up; all kinds of chaos in the meantime. Had those things not happened, it would have taken two or three years anyway; it was labour intensive. My intention was not just to build a house. I also wanted to learn all the bits: how do you design a house, how do you do the footings, how do you do the concrete work, how do you do the blockwork, *et cetera*. I actually wanted to learn all the skills on the way.

Did you actually design this yourself?

John: Yes; I did. The only thing I didn't do was to learn how to operate a JCB and dig the trenches. Everything else – I did it, I got it. I had an architect check out the plans, but basically they're my plans.

Did he make many alterations?

John: Very little, because I'd gone for a very simple design. There wasn't anything very much to alter. Right at the start, I'd gone along to the Building Centre in London and bought a stack of books – everything I could lay my hands on about Building Regs and standard stuff like that, plus a few selfbuild books. But they were all American, so they weren't much use.

I learnt partly by reading books before I did the design work. But I found I learnt as much by getting hold of other people's plans. Seeing how their plans were laid out taught me more than any single book.

How did you get hold of those plans?

John: I had friends who were building houses. I found everybody I could lay my hands on, mainly rebuilding derelicts – this was over in Wales. So I learnt from their experience.

I learnt partly from books, but from people doing it live was the best source of information for me. Plus I had enough practical experience – I was not practically inept.

You'd been a kind of DIY person beforehand, had you?

John: Sort of. I'd actually spent a number of years living on narrow boats and converting them. I'd learnt a number of practical skills, especially with timber. But plumbing, central heating, wiring, gas – all of that's involved with boats.

I did a conversion on a seventy-foot narrow boat. It sounds sickeningly together, but I bought a hull, sunk, for £15 – it had a six-foot tree growing out of one end. Five years later it had everything on it, and I sold it for £4,000, which was then a record for a wooden hulled narrow boat. It was rather nice, but I spent years on it. And the house was a bit the same: it was very much a labour of love. Doing it to learn and doing it the way I wanted it to be was more important than it making financial sense. Which was just as well, because it didn't make an awful lot of financial sense in the end.

How long did the project take you?

John: We moved on site in a caravan in '76. The one acre field was completely overgrown, so we had to clear a way in and lay tracks to get a caravan in. We spent two years building and got the shell up and weatherproof. This is myself and Sally. We split the work fifty-fifty so Sally really did work. We just had this agreement that we shared whatever we were doing. The Welsh delivery guys were astonished to see this woman laying blocks. And I was carrying the blocks for her because I was strongest. It made more sense for me to carry and her to lay. We did that quite a lot.

How did you split the work up?

John: I had this thing that I wanted to learn everything, and I had more physical skills than Sally. So I did everything. She tended to do whatever was more effective for her to do. She, in many ways, was more efficient than I was. She could actually lay blocks faster than I could. I tended to be researching and doing the next bit, while she was doing a lot of the physical work on the last bit. So for example, when we got to laying stone fireplaces, it was me that had to go off and research how the hell do you design and build a stone fireplace – what shape, throat, chimney, all of that stuff – while she was still going round laying the blocks. So there was an inequality there. I actually learnt far more skills than she did, because she wasn't as interested as I was in learning the skills. She was more interested in getting a house built.

So you got the shell up in two years. What happened then?

John: We ran out of money. We started the project with £5,000 each. The plot cost £2,250 – this is in Wales in '76.

Had you searched around a lot for a plot?

John: We had spent a year looking all over Wales for a plot, because everybody said that you can't buy a one acre plot, out in the countryside, with trees and with a stream, with Planning Permission to build – that's ridiculous. So it took a lot of searching to find one, and that cost us a lot of money – it cost us thousands of pounds to live whilst we were looking around.

We finally found it through an estate agent. How it actually happened was really stupid, the way these things often are. We had found it earlier, but didn't like the setting, thought it was disgusting, and forgot it. We rediscovered it a number of months later; went back and looked at it more closely; and thought "Well yes, it is like a scrap heap, but if we clear the cars away and the rubbish, this is actually an excellent site. It's got everything. Great!".

Then there were legal hassles. The plot only joined the road at a point: you could have a footpath, but not get a vehicle on the plot. The ownership of the bits of adjoining land had been lost, so legally we couldn't be sure that we had vehicle access.

How did you get over that one then?

John: We took out an insurance policy that said that, if anyone subsequently came and laid claim to those bits of land that would deny us access, the policy would pay us a lot of money, that should be more than enough to buy the land off anybody. Of course, no-one ever claimed them.

What happened when you'd run out of money?

John: We had to attempt to earn a living out in rural Wales, and save the capital to buy the materials. Basically, we never cracked that one. I did building work; Sally went and did a job at an agricultural college.

Were you coming back in the evening and working on the house?

John: Theoretically, yes. In fact, we weren't. The whole momentum and energy had been lost.

Basically, building the house had overloaded our relationship. Because we spent so much time together, the relationship then blew apart a year or so after we'd stopped building. Sally decided to move out. We then had to sort out what we were doing about the money.

We had the half-built house valued by two different estate agents, because we knew it was anybody's guess what a half-built house is worth. They were miles apart, so we took the average of the two valuations. I agreed to buy out her share in a year's time, one way or the other. In fact, my parents stepped in to the rescue, because by this time I was into a heavy depression, I was down and out. My parents agreed to buy out Sally's share because otherwise I would have had to sell the house. It's not worth selling a half-built house. It's a silly move. They bought out her share, which I think at that point, in '79, was worth eight or nine thousand pounds.

So then I was in a half-built house with no capital and no job. It took me a year or two to claw my way out of the depression. Then I realized that the easiest way to carry on was to borrow money from the bank against the security of the house. This would enable me to buy the materials and pay friends to help do the building.

John Seymour's house with Garage / Workshop

It was quite easy to get the bank to agree to this. The hard part was getting me to do it, because I'd never borrowed money in my life. I was terrified at the very thought of borrowing money. Once I'd done that, it then started moving again. It took years to finish it. It was 1980 when my parents had finally bought out Sally's share. It took me another two years to finish the main house.

I then spent another two years building the garage and workshop, in between going to Bristol on courses.

I sold it in '85 for £44,000. The people I sold it to did like it a lot. It was like their dream house.

Were you pleased with the way the energy effectiveness worked out?

John: Very pleased. We had an Aga solid fuel boiler, 20,000 btu's, and thermostatic rad valves on all the radiators. £120 a year gave us all our central heating and hot water. We also had a little stone fireplace that we burnt wood on, but that was mainly to have a fire to sit around in the evening. So that was for aesthetics, not for heat.

The other thing was the thermal flywheel effect on the house. For the inner leaf I didn't use aerated blocks, Thermalite; I used solid concrete blocks inside. I had a 3" cavity with 1½" of polystyrene in the cavity, so I wanted the thermal flywheel effect of the inner leaf. [That is, the inner leaf stored heat, warming the house when the temperature dropped but cooling it on hot days.] And that was quite pronounced. The house held a very nice temperature.

Also, the way I designed it, the house faces due south. Fifty percent of the window area was south facing. In summer, the roof overhang at the eaves shaded the upstairs windows. In winter, the sun drops and you get a passive solar gain through the windows. It was a very sunny house. In winter, the sun just blasted through the house and heated it up.

Were the windows double glazed?

John: No; I'd run out of money at that stage. I did use second-hand ¼" plate glass which gives a slight gain.

The central heating was designed to be augmented by solar heating, so I actually did all of the plumbing for that. But again, I ran out of money, and I didn't have the money to put in the solar panels.

What were some of the particular features of the house?

John: The stone fireplace. It sounds a bit crazy in retrospect, but I cast all of the grate. I made the wooden patterns and had them cast just how I wanted them. Then under the floor, there were pipes to the outside to draw in air without causing draughts.

I made the cupboards in the kitchen. By that time, I'd got some wood machinery together, with a 6" planer/thicknesser/saw bench. I was into the joys of wood machining.

I did the stairs as well. I did all the woodwork for the banisters and the staircase. The stairs were pretty difficult; they were the trickiest piece of joinery. It was a dog-legged staircase, but it was all in one basic unit, and getting your mind round this, how it all works – let alone having it all work without squeaking like hell – was tricky.

That must be an understatement! What were the other tricky bits?

John: Central heating design: doing the full heat-loss calculations and sizing; and the plumbing system; and designing it all so that it works.

The Solid Fuel Advisory people did a course, and I went and did the course. I was surprised how complicated designing a heating system is. To get all the problems out, so that it not only works but is optimal, was a real hassle.

And the other thing that was really tricky was plastering. That's a pain, to actually get it so that you can do big surfaces well. By the time I'd finished the house, I'd pretty well mastered plastering, but the first rooms were tricky. And I got a professional plasterer in to show me how to do it. I paid him to come in for a few hours – it's an excellent idea. We started in the bathroom. Choose the smallest room, the smallest wall – get a trained plasterer to teach you on the smallest walls and then you can take it on from there.

It's definitely tricky. You need high physical aptitude. You need to be bright because you've got to get your mind around all of the practical things: the mix, the consistency, and where you're going to start on the wall and where you end up, getting the corners, and things like that. You need to be physically adroit, for the actual physical process of doing it. You need to be strong, because walls, and ceilings particularly, are killers on the arms.

What did you use?

John: I used sand-and-cement over the blockwork and a timber straight-edge to get it flattish. Then I used two layers of skim. One layer filled it in, but it was still a bit rough. The second layer gave it a smooth finish.

The finish on the outside is unusual. Was it easy to do?

John: Yes; it was a doddle to do.

The way it came about:

We discovered by accident, dropping mortar onto polystyrene, that mortar actually bonded very well onto polystyrene. Now that got me into playing with "Well, this is interesting. If you can render polystyrene, what else can you do?". And that eventually led to the garage, which was a whole building based on rendering polystyrene. But along the route to developing that, we discovered that it was quite easy to make render look like stone.

All you do is put on a first coat, 6:1 standard render job. You roughly begin to mark out stones, occasional corners, and it's "Lets put a thick bit on here, and let's have a few lines in there". The second coat you put on, and you build it up some more, again using trowel and rubber-gloved hands. So you put in yet more thick bits here, and a line there, and an edge there, just to show what it would look like. You need to know stonework to do that. I knew roughly the kinds of patterning.

You put on the second coat, you trowel it, and then you leave it to stiffen up a little. Now at that point it still has trowel marks on and looks disgusting. While it's still soft, you get a 6″ brush and some water, and go over it, and take out all the trowel marks; and this gives it a whitewashed-stone effect. The brushing removes all the trowel marks, so all you see is the rough underlying shapes, which are suggestive of stone outlines. It's actually quite quick to do. And as long as you get the basic stonework patterns right, it comes out very convincing. Everybody who walked up to the house was sure that it was a stone house.

It's painted with Sandtex. I actually painted it red because William Morris is one of my heroes. The Red House was his house that he designed. I just couldn't resist doing mine red.

I feel I learnt a hell of a lot building the house, and I will probably go and build another house.

What sorts of things would you do differently another time?

John: Personally, I overdosed on physical work. The amount of physical work was horrific – 60 tonnes of blocks to be manipulated by hand. So by the time I'd finished the house, I was sick to death of physical work. I'd had enough of it, and I never wanted to do any more physical work in the rest of my life.

So what's the answer to that then – to subcontract it or to do a different style?

John: A bit of both. I didn't realize at the outset just how labour intensive a labour intensive house was going to be. So I would not do it so labour intensive, unless I was going to subcontract out a lot of the work. I would probably use a mixture of timber-frame and solid materials if I was going to be doing it another time.

I wouldn't do that kind of project again without having enough money at the start. That was such a back-breaker.

I built it without scaffolding because we never had the money for scaffolding. We built it from the inside, on drums and planks. You get the joists up on the first floor, then you bring the 45 gallon drums up and put your planks on them and go up to the roof, and so on.

When we got to do the rendering, we did in effect make a kind of temporary scaffolding, which we could move around. The kind of scaffolding we made hung off ladders. You can get things which hang off a ladder, which hold planks between ladders. We made that up out of bits of wood – a funny wooden contraption hanging between a pair of ladders.

What about the drains?

John: We put in a septic tank. It digests the shit. Plastic tanks were new at that time. We built a huge container: concrete base, block walls rendered, various chambers. Sewage comes in, trickles down through stones, gets digested, then the water trickles away, off to a soakaway.

How often did you have to have it emptied?

John: While I was there, it was working for three or four years. I never had to do anything to it. I believe that you do gradually get an accumulation of sediment and you do need to clear them out every so often, but I was told this would be once every ten years or so.

What about the rainwater?

John: There were simply soakaways.

What sort of soil was it?

John: About 9″ of loam on the top. Underneath that, it was straight clay, with bits of rock underneath. We used over-sized foundations because clay tends to move.

What sort of floor was it?

John: It was solid. We put 2″ of polystyrene on the concrete slab and a 2¹/₂″ screed on top, so that the floor was insulated. It felt relatively warm underfoot. And that worked very well. It had to be a thick screed over polystyrene, or it might have cracked up. We had tiled floors.

Any other points?

John: I did quite a few of the courses at the Centre for Alternative Technology. I guess I learnt quite a bit from them, although I used very little of it in the house. If I built another house, I would have the confidence from this one to be much more experimental in what I took on. I was very conscious that I was learning and that you can make really expensive mistakes when you're learning. So that's why I played quite safe with this house.

I would recommend that to anybody – play fairly safe if it's the first time you're doing it. A lot of friends, building over there in Wales, made disastrously expensive mistakes. I had a simple plan and I stuck to it, and that worked well.

The other thing I did, which was a bit over the top, but seemed worth it:

In the roof, I'd got in the joists 4″ of insulation. But then in the rafters, I again put 4″ of insulation. So there was double insulation up there. But when you do that, when you insulate between the rafters, you have to put a polythene damp proof membrane inside. Otherwise you get damp, you get dewpoint achieved in the insulation, and that will rot the timbers. That worked very well.

No problems building the chimney?

John: Problems of severe fear whilst building the chimney; yes! It was bloody high and I'd erected a temporary wooden scaffold up there to do it. But some of it got quite hairy, particularly when we had low flying jets there. I remember one day, Sally was up there, and we'd taken the scaffold away – it was right at the end – and this jet comes over, really low and fast, WWHAAMMM!! She went spread-eagled flat on the chimney. I was afraid she was going to fall off.

A big problem with the house was because it was so high. All of the slating on the roof I did in a harness with a rope. If I'd fallen off, there was no scaffolding to stop me. The least that I'd have done would be to break some limbs, and I could have killed myself. So doing the roof was painfully slow, because of the harness business.

The slating was Welsh slate, second-hand but very expensive. In fact, it's random width slating which is even harder to get. The widths are not regular; it's visually much more attractive. Random width is a lot easier than you might think. (Random length is a real mind-bender because the batten spacing is bananas.) The key thing is to keep the cracks a minimum distance away from the cracks in the course below. Sometimes a wide slate goes over two cracks.

What was your motive for building your own house?

John: At least two different motives.

For me, it was like a major daydream. It was something I'd always wanted to do – and to learn the skills.

Sally wanted to have a smallholding – that was her dream. She liked growing things. We couldn't afford a smallholding. We thought that, if we built a house and sold it, that would just give us enough money. So there was a financial motive there.

Initially, it was very exciting. I got a real buzz out of doing it. The early part of it, getting the shell up – a lot of it was very exciting, very rewarding. It's like pioneering. You're actually doing something for real, and creating something that wasn't there. It was a great buzz.

After that, the sheer amount of work made keeping the motivation going very difficult.

What about the construction of the garage?

John: It's timber-frame, mainly 3″ by 2″, covered with polystyrene, and rendered both inside and out – 2″ polystyrene nailed on the outside. At the joins, to stop the rendering cracking, you put 4″ hessian scrim, held by the galvanized nails. And inside, you render in between the timber framework.

That's an optional extra, isn't it?

John: Not really. Because of fire, I'd say it was a necessity. In a fire, polystyrene is so lethal. A few lungfulls of that – well, it kills very fast.

That's basically it, a simple timber-framed building with a nice effect inside. Using this kind of building technology, you could make housing that was so cost effective you wouldn't believe it. The fact that it was not a cavity wall was irrelevant, as far as I can see. It was perfectly weatherproof. We didn't have any problems with anything.

I had to really hassle the building inspectors to be allowed to put polystyrene insulation in the cavity wall. I had to sit down and work out all the U-value calculations in order to satisfy them. It's standard practice now, but at that time nobody had ever done it before in that district.

How well did you get on with the building inspector? Was he helpful or was he a hindrance?

John: He was actually neutral. This guy wanted an easy life, so he showed up just the minimum amount that he had to.

Have you any particular advice to pass onto people who are contemplating building their own house?

John: I believe there was a study in the States, where selfbuilding is much more common than it is here, which showed that a lot of the couples that set out to build a house together split up before they finished. I think people ought to know that. You spend all of your time together. Unless you stick to strict sex roles, and the woman never gets her hands dirty, you spend all of your time together; and if there are any bits of your relationship that don't work, they're going to blow up right in your face.

I tend to think that it's only quite exceptional individuals that will do the whole thing well themselves. I just think it's very demanding. There's an awful lot to do. You have to be very clear at the outset, that what you're taking on is a mammoth task, and you plan it to minimize the hassle factors. Keep it very simple. It probably means going for a timber-frame building. Design everything to keep the effort minimal, because otherwise you're just going to find it overwhelming. I did it the long way round and it was totally overwhelming; I wouldn't do it again like that.

There's the obvious thing that, if you don't have enough money, you're going to have nightmarish problems. I was stupid. I didn't do proper cost estimates, and I should have done. I naïvely thought there was probably just enough money to do it, and of course, there wasn't anything like.

I wish I'd known about getting a mortgage on a selfbuild at the time. I thought it would be virtually impossible, but of course, it's not, it's relatively straightforward.

4

LINA
AND VIC

BUILDING ON BOTH SIDES OF THE ATLANTIC

I FIRST MET Vic by chance in a travel agents on Malta. He had been commissioned to sail a boat back to Holland, but the sails had torn in a gale so he was having to leave the boat and fly home. I was returning from a holiday. We booked adjacent seats on the plane, and it transpired that we had selfbuild as a common interest. A few months later, he and his wife, Lina, left Britain to build themselves their last house in Maine, USA. A couple of days before they left, I had the interview with them recorded below.

Vic met and married Lina in occupied Germany after the Second World War. (Lina was German, with a Danish mother.) During the course of their married life, they have built themselves four bungalows: on Mersea Island, Essex, 1962–63, at Levenheath, Essex, 1976–78, in Florida, USA, 1980, and another one next door a couple of years later. Some account of their American experiences is given, not because it is directly relevant, but because it does help to put the British experiences into a context.

Vic and Lina also build boats! They have lived in those too, and sailed to far off places. Some of our conversation was about this. Again, this may not seem particularly relevant. But selfbuild is not, in the first instance, about knowledge or skill, but rather it's about attitude. Self-reliance is needed to build both your own boat and your own home.

Like many other selfbuilders, Vic and Lina had first acquired building skills doing a house restoration, and our conversation started with that topic.

☆   ☆   ☆   ☆   ☆

How did you first get involved in building?

Vic: No money – in the sense that you want something but you haven't got the means to do it the orthodox way, to have it built.

So how far back is this then?

Vic: Well, it goes back to the very first house we owned, 1952 or '53 – something like that. It was a house that had been empty for 20 years, which needed restoration. We did a total restoration job.

What you don't know, you learn.

So you learnt the hard way, just through doing it?

Vic: Yes. If you have to pay a plumber your week's wages for twenty minutes of his work, you learn quickly.

Were you working in a job?

Vic: Yes; we had to. We were working on the house evenings and weekends. Because of that, the job went on for two to three years.

Were you trying to live in the house at the same time?

Vic: Yes; we did live in it – we lived with orange boxes for furniture. We learnt that it was better to pay cash, to work from actual money, rather than borrow money to do major operations.

What work were you doing there – electrics, plumbing. . .?

Vic: Yes. I've always done electrics and I've always done plumbing – well, not always plumbing. I did actually have a plumber for a repair. I did all the ground work, I dug all the thing out, about thirty feet of dirt – for him to come along and spend twenty minutes and charge me a week of my wages. From that moment on I became a plumber! I do everything. In those days we even used to mix our own concrete by hand. Gradually we got older and wiser.

Things like plastering you learnt through actually doing it?

Vic: Well, yes – plastering, in the sense that I always did small quantities in restoration work. It wasn't until I happened to buy a piece of land next to a retired bricklayer and plasterer that I was really shown how to set the job out properly. He said afterwards I was a good plasterer – I had good hands. That was praise indeed from him because he was very good.

But until then, I tended to make do, just on an adequacy basis – it was almost good enough. But knowing what I now know, it was probably not good enough.

You can't impart the secret then?

Vic: No; not really. He showed me how to set it out. And of course, it was like always, like everything – so simple and logical once you know how. It was quick and easy, but having done it – great. I've never looked back.

What do you mean by 'setting it out'?

Vic: Setting your walls out, so that all your corners are right angles and everything is plumb and true.

So if the wall is a little out of true, how do you set it out?

Vic: It depends how bad it is. If you've got, say, up to $3/4''$ out of true, you've just got to correct that, to produce the corrected surface.

If you were doing a wall, you'd set your corner out with three pads – a splodge of stuff [sand-and-cement] with a piece of, say, masonite [American term for hardboard] pushed into it – one near the bottom of the wall, another splodge in the middle, another splodge at the top. You'd plumb between the masonite surfaces to make a vertical screed of plaster. You repeat that, so that you've got a series of vertical screeds. I use, I suppose, a five-foot board.

So do you have another series of pads nearly five feet along?

Vic: Yes.

[The wall is divided into vertical sections by a series of plaster ridges nearly five-foot apart. These ridges are trued up in line and called 'screeds'. Then plaster is applied (or 'layed on') to one section of the wall. The screeding board bridges a section, with each end on a screed. By scraping the board upwards from floor to ceiling, the plaster in that section is levelled off with the screeds.]

It depends on the weather you see. It depends how quickly it's going off. If it's high summer, and everything is drying as fast as it can, you're virtually working a panel at a time: laying it on and then screeding it off. And then doing the next. And then coming back at some elapsed time interval that you decide, and then floating it.

And obviously, you get used to the consistency of the mix.

Do you set out all these masonite pads first?

Vic: I wouldn't do all the wall; no. It depends on the temperature. If it's in the middle of winter and it's quite cold, possibly do the whole wall. In the summer, you just keep ahead, so that it's going off enough. So that when you use these surfaces to ride on, they don't give way, or collapse. And you join them up. They become part of the finish, they are fresh enough and green enough. Whereas, in the middle of January, it will take all night for them to go off enough for you to use them for levelling pads.

You take the masonite out, and come back and fill in between the screeds. You float it flat.

But it sounds far more difficult than it actually is.

So it's a case of having a method and knowing what you're doing?

Vic: Yes. The modern way is with plasterboard [dry lining] and most of it's skimmed. But if you're doing it this way, traditionally I suppose you'd call this, mixing it is important, getting the right consistency. I find with a concrete mixer that's fine.

Your mix is important, and that depends what you're putting it on. Obviously putting it on to an old brick wall is difficult; it needs a lot of care. If you're into Unibond – great. But if you're putting it onto clinker block, anything like that, it hangs on beautifully. I don't lose anything now.

Then with the Thistle I put two-thirds of Thistle and a third of Sirapite. ['Thistle' and 'Sirapite' are proprietary names for finish plaster.] It gives you a better finish. The old plasterer gave me the idea. He suggested it – he didn't *tell* you anything. I used to have a paddle on my drill; he would always mix by hand. But I mixed by paddle because I was both mixing and spreading, and you begin to get a little tired with the hand mixing.

When you're putting the final coat on, if you hit it just right – you put it on right, you spread it on, and then you come back and almost polish it – if you hit it right, it's gorgeous, it's really lovely.

Do you use browning at all?

Vic: I've used all sorts. I prefer Thistle finish and a normal, orthodox ground coat: sand-and-cement. That's a personal preference.

What about the ceiling? You had no trouble skimming the ceilings?

Vic: No; not really. Although rarely today do you do that – or do *I* do that. More often than not, it's artex. (Although in America, artex has only recently become common. 'Popcorn' is now a popular pattern.)

In America, most of the walls are stud walls with plasterboard. They fill in the seams; the seams are all tapered edge plasterboard. So you buy readymixed infill, polyfilla type stuff, in 62 lb tubs; and you run in some tape with the infill stuff, sand it when it's dry, and paint it. Then individual owners like to add wallpaper and so on.

In fact, in Florida, I did a lot of artexing, using not artex, using this infill mix – creamy polyfilla you'd call it.

Anyway, you started off doing this renovation. When did you do your first completely new build?

Vic: That was 1962, at East Mersea. It wasn't a hundred percent; we had that started, the foundations and some walls done. That wasn't a total one, but it was almost all my own house.

It was my own design. I went to a large building company in Colchester, gave them my drawing, and we took it from there. They did a quarter of the thing. We had a disagreement. They didn't do what they said they'd do, and what they did do they did in the wrong place.

They didn't put the whole shell up, and we did everything inside. We put the roof on. That was a straightforward roof, a rectangle.

The whole job was over seven or eight months. We had all sorts of aggro – law-suits – and I refused to pay some. I lost out in the end.

Anyway, with the bungalow built, you went in for some boat building?

Vic: Well, yes. In East Mersea, our place became a boat yard. We built our own. In the same way that you build a house, you build a boat for yourself, and you use it, and you sell it.

How did you get into boat building?

Vic: I always had boats. The first boat was a 26′ Morecombe Bay prawner, which needed some work doing on it. We worked on her, and sailed. We built another boat called a Folk boat. We had the shell up to the gunwales built by a boat builder. The shell was totally empty. We designed our own ideas on to what was an orthodox Folk boat hull. A Folk boat is a racing class boat, and it's usually ultra light. But we didn't want to race; we wanted to cruise. So we built her to go across oceans. Having done it, and having made her very strong, beautiful and so on, we found that, in cruising to, say, Holland with her and living on her for a couple of weeks, she was too small for living. She was a beautiful sea boat. This one was 25′ long.

So we then built a 50′ catamaran, with a lot of accommodation – again, our own idea. We're going back a long way – we're talking of 1965. We started the catamaran in '66, I think. There were no books or rules to guide you about catamarans. It was just ideas then; they were opinions. It was the early days.

So when did you build the one that you did go round the world in?

Vic: We launched her in 1970, the 50′ catamaran. We didn't go right round the world. We sailed to lots of places.

Llara of Colne

Our idea was "If we've got to mend it, we'd better build it strong so that it doesn't break – because it's going to be us that's going to mend it". That proved successful in the sense that it didn't break and she did all that we wanted to do in her. She didn't leak. We hit various rocks and reefs and things over the years and she didn't break. Modern thinking since then has been towards lightness and speed, so that the catamarans today are the fastest things on the water. But they weigh one third of what mine did. Rocks would take the bottom out of them half the time.

What were the hulls made from?

Vic: Everything was wood. Plywood planking. We used a 'V' form of hull. At the time, there was nothing to relate to. We were investing a lot of money that we didn't have, into something that might be sailable, might not be sailable. We were pushing our luck. Nowadays, it would be classified as being on the edge of technology. What we were doing was utilizing fishing boat theory – if it was that thick, it didn't break. We continued along those lines. Our thinking was "I'm building a different concept. Maybe I'll try this – see how it works". As it happened, when the first gale came, we were in a very difficult position, and I was running round the boat seeing if the paint was cracking anywhere to indicate that we were in trouble. The boats take a beating sometimes that you don't really believe they can take. But the boat is, in fact, far stronger than you, the crew. You are the weak link.

The catamaran was an experiment. We were involved in the quality of life, rather than earning money. We had a shop at the time; we were doing 14-hour days with the boat, on the basis that we had a pile of wood that we'd bought that had to end up as a boat and be launched – or it was worth nothing. We ran out of money as everyone does. We launched her in an incomplete state, with no sails for example. We then earned a bit more money, made the sails ourselves, and went for a sail on August Bank Holiday Monday, 1970. And everything worked well. We had about twelve volunteers, on the day, to help us sail. She didn't capsize, she sailed quickly. We had a base from which to develop.

We sailed six years. We stayed in the Atlantic – the Caribbean, the Bahamas, America, the Atlantic, the North Sea, Heligoland, Portugal, Spain, Gibraltar, the Med. We sailed along the African coast. There's a lot of piracy there. We weren't armed. Boats disappeared.

Anyway, you came back. Where did you build your next bungalow?

Vic: In Levenheath, in Essex. We did one a hundred percent ourselves. We mixed every shovel of concrete, we dug all the trenches. This was in the dry summer of '76. We dug the foundations out by hand; it took 31 days with pick and shovel.

The point is, we'd come back from sailing (we'd been sailing for about five or six years), hyperinflation had taken place, and the little bit of money that we'd got from selling the East Mersea bungalow bought a piece of land and a few bricks. So literally, we were faced with doing everything ourselves. You get older, and facing up to concrete mixing, you don't want to do it any more.

But we spent 31 days pickaxing – it wasn't digging. Below about 12″ down, you came to what I would call glacial stone. You couldn't put a fork in it in any way whatsoever. You had to pick, and break through it. We collected the stones and used them later. I'd have got a JCB in, but we didn't have any money. What do you do? Do you go out and earn some money to get a JCB in? – No; get on with it.

Lina and I mixed all the concrete with a mixer. We got materials cheap, and it paid us to mix our own. At the same time, Lina was digging the garden and kept us in vegetables. We had to come from nothing, again. All we had was a bit of land and the first pile of bricks, and that's all we had.

Did you think of borrowing money?

Vic: Yes; but they don't lend it to people who have been wandering about for six years in a boat.

I drew the plans for this one on the boat. We were living on the boat.

You felt confident about designing it?

Vic: Yes. Although it was our design, we had to conform to what they wanted, compared to the houses on either side. We were doing it from a limited budget. It's pretty conventional, though the windows were large relative to the local standards.

I find that, if you design almost anything, just purely in the design and the submission of the drawings, you'll be finding out how you're going to do it. You're going through "I wonder how I'm going to solve that problem".

I first submitted the plans and had them rejected on the grounds of lack of justification. I had to get a civil engineer, or whatever he's called these days, to do the calculations for submission, regarding joist loads and so on. They were able to recommend the man who happened to live right next door to them. So that was resolved very quickly and quite readily.

Vic and Lina's bungalow at Levenheath

And it was a bungalow?

Vic: Yes. Though after we'd moved in, I put skylights in the roof. In fact, I made them, I didn't buy them. I made them from some old beds left over, solid oak. We got two more bedrooms up there, and another bathroom and a little box-room.

We had a double plumbing system in this place. We'd got no money. I did a chimney breast incorporating three chimneys: an open fire, the eventual Parkray to run central skirting-board heating, and backing in there, on the other side, is the Aga cooker. We couldn't afford the capital outlay for these. That was the thinking in the design at the time – to add them later.

They were big rooms; the lounge was 31′ by 18′. The doors I made from offcuts. They were quite effective – they were individual, shall I say.

I bought a hundred yards of floor tiles cheap, and I used them wherever I could: table surface, hallway, the whole of the kitchen.

You can do this when you're building for yourself. You can see cheap stuff, and you can think how to utilize it.

Vic: Yes; that's right.

The bathroom was quite a *de luxe* bathroom. It was 18′ by 8′, with shower compartment up one end.

I built the stairs from bits left over from the boat. I had to conform to the 100 mm rubbish – no gap. I had an open type of hand-rail. I made it decorative. And then, for him to pass it, I screwed sheets of plywood up onto it. And then took them down when he'd gone. And the same with the gaps between the treads: they had to be reduced to 100 mm. I put some dowelling pieces in. I like open stairs. I haven't got six kids. If someone who buys it has, then that's their problem, isn't it?

All I've built have been bungalows. This is the nearest to a house, a chalet bungalow if you like.

How have you got on with building inspectors?

Vic: In England, not very well I suppose. They didn't, to me, come forth. They were prepared to sit on their chair and say "That is not adequate", but with no reasons other than "It does not comply with the Building Regulation number eight". They didn't say "Make that nine-by-three [inches] instead of two-by-eight, and it will be alright". So we didn't have a good relationship. Although, I remember, February 8th one year, I saw one of them smile; that was quite an occasion.

But we didn't have any screaming rows or anything. It was just a lack of helpfulness. No helpfulness; none. In fact, during the Levenheath one, the building inspector was complaining to a neighbour of mine how long I was taking over the job. But of course, he wasn't paying the bills. I was doing this from cash earned. I was doing jobs contract-build to Lucas, making traction battery boxes. This was on the basis that, when Lucas's wanted some boxes, I stopped bricklaying and made their boxes. This allowed me to take cash from them and buy more bricks. So we paid for that house, literally from earnings and the initial land purchase.

How long did it take?

Vic: Two-and-a-half years.

Later on, you built a couple of bungalows in the States. Do they have building inspectors over there?

Vic: Yes; it's much the same. The point about the building inspection over there is that they are empowered to come at any time. The stages are much closer together. Mine did, in fact, arrive every day. If he didn't come, you were quite surprised: "Oh, Werner hasn't come". They come and check almost everything, although there are some major points at which they have to sign the ticket. But we were very, very fortunate with this particular building inspector. If they fail anything, they say you've done it wrong, and there is what's called a 'ten dollar recall'. Before you can proceed any further, you have to correct it, and he has to come and approve it – and that's a ten dollar fine. But he didn't charge me at all. I got tremendous advice; he was extremely helpful. He stayed a friend – a Christmas card friend and letters once a year.

The Florida ones were after the British ones.

They were both my own design and build, to suit the plot. This was an area of 60 square miles which had been given zoning permission on condition that a grid of roads was put through it. In the beginning, when that area was being developed, the Planning Permissions – call them that – were that, until there was town water through, one in three plots could be developed. When the sewer came through, two plots in every three could be developed.

Vic and Lina's bungalow in Florida

Before the town water came through, where were the houses getting their water from?

Vic: You had to drill for it. We didn't drill it but we had to commission a driller to come and do it. And then the Public Health Authority come along and say that the water is pure. We had to go down 100′. It only takes an hour. It cost about $650; that includes the pipe, and pressure system (a pump and compressor). It's very common in rural areas.

In Maine locally, there's no Planning Permissions as such. But you have to give them the floor area, how many bedrooms, and so, potentially, how many people are going to be using it – for the foul water that is going to be running away. The drain field has to be approved; but the structure doesn't. You just say "I am going to build a four-bedroomed, 3,000-square-foot house like this". No building control. That's Maine (Florida's different). They specify the size of the drain field and the septic tank size – 1,000 or 3,000 gallons, whatever they say. You don't have any choice.

You would plan your foundations with all the services underneath the slab – if you do a slab, which is fifty percent of the time. All your copper tube is in single lengths; in other words, you can't join under the concrete slab.

How do you get the long lengths?

Vic: Well, you buy the copper tube in 60′ coils. You bring them up at each end above the surface; they're malleable. You bring them up, two stubs, and then you join above the concrete. You put that in a cupboard, or within a wall is the commonest thing. The copper pipes are your distribution, hot and cold water.

You have to identify the pipes before you bury them under concrete. Of course, it does happen: clever little kids come along and change the reds with the blues. But we found that, by putting an air line down them before doing any connections, we checked them out.

Then of course, the building inspector will come. Everything has to be sealed. All the fittings have to be on, and he comes to the washing machine taps and he pressurizes that for his test. It has to hold 62 lbs per square inch for the prescribed time. If not, it fails and life is difficult because you have to find out where it's failed.

There are no header tanks except if you do it yourself. It's just a direct, pressurized distribution system. It works.

You've got a hot water cylinder into which there's an immersion heater. In the Florida one, it was a 64'-long building, and it used to pressure a shower at the far end. We had no problem at all.

What about their electrics over there?

Vic: You're dealing with 110 volts.

Do they use an earth?

Vic: Yes. But they don't use a ring main. We're ahead of them in many respects. In fact, I take over things like terminal blocks – they've never seen them in Florida. And junction boxes – they never use them. They get two wires together, put a cap over and screw it. We used to do that here twenty-five years ago, but it was banned.

But your pumps and your cooking range, and the deep freeze I think, they work on 220 volts. So you pick up two bus bars – two hot wires – a white neutral and a separate earth. Black is hot there. The 110 is safer. By the cleverness of the electronics these days, it's even halved again within the equipment, so you get hit with 55 volts.

The meter is outside, as it is here now. They give you the cans [meter boxes], and you put your own heavy duty wires down into the cans. They bring the meter along. They connect there; then do their tests; check the adequacy of the grounding system.

You supply the earth yourself do you?

Vic: Yes. Well, you go and buy it; it's an eight-foot rod. It's got to be vertically stuck in the ground. It's not hard work: you're dealing with compacted sand down there.

In a reasonably sized town there will be four or five hypermarkets where you can buy everything you want – except perhaps for bricks – at highly competitive prices. The advice in the stores is extremely good, technically – particularly on electrical stuff. There is a guy at these hypermarkets whose responsibility is the electrical department.

It's not the sort of thing you get over here?

Vic: It's totally different. Mainly because the salesmen are on no wages, commission only. They're anxious to please. When you go in the door – "Hi, Victor. What do we want this morning?", and it's all positive. "We've got this, and we've done that, and this is new"; and so on. And I say "I'm an idiot, and what gauge of wire do you recommend for this?", or "What does the rule book say about this?". And they say "Oh, you want a number two or a number four"; and so on. They know the answers.

One factor must be that a lot more people build their own houses over there?

Vic: Yes. But a lot of it is subcontracted. They talk of "I built my house", and they really mean "I acted as contractor, and organized the subcontractors".

Because huge amounts of money are borrowed in America, there are a lot of controls about being your own subcontractor. The banks don't just give you lots of money and let you go away and sort it out. They involve themselves; the loan officers keep an eye on it.

Most people in America, 95% maybe, maximize their borrowing rather than minimize it. They will commission an architect to design something for them, and then the architect stays involved. The owner reserves the right to approve the contracts, for example, 'Fred shall be the bricklayer', or 'Albert shall do the framework'.

When you designed your Florida houses, were they in an American style?

Vic: Yes. You tend to look at that which is around you. There is no point in building a palace next to a fish and chip shop. And again, you need to know the local rules, which say that you can't build within eight feet of the boundary.

What about the walls? I imagine they are timber?

Vic: Most building in Florida, I would say, is frame: frame with a cladding. That varies: it can be timber, aluminium or brick. Brick is high class; it's then advertised as 'real brick'. The main reason, of course, is that timber is relatively cheap. And the studs are all pre-cut – $92^5/_8''$, come in bundles. Because you've got five hypermarkets dealing in these things, you phone them all. You must have a phone. You make good deals, all the time. But they are not lumber yards in the sense that you get them here. They're supermarkets selling lumber. It's good quality – I made lots of furniture from the spruce, straight-grained. Then they have impregnated yellow pine.

You can fabricate benches, tables, chairs, cupboards, everything. It's very easily done. It's worth doing, in the sense that it's cheap furniture and relatively attractive. I always used to polish and wax it.

We build boats, right? That tends to be:

"What have you done this morning?"

"Oh, I fitted this bit of wood" – with four curves in it, and a rebate along its inside edge and so on. I enjoy that type of work more than anything. I enjoy making one-off pieces of furniture for one-off places. I don't like mass production work. I like to think it out, plan it, execute it and make it so that when I go back I think "I made that. I like that. It's still good; it's still working. The ideas were good. I wouldn't have done it any differently today".

How much was Lina helping you?

Vic: A hundred percent. Although when we built in Levenheath, we had to eat as well, so she got a three day job in Colchester in Boots. I was doing the Lucas job to earn money for capital goods.

Lina, entering from the kitchen where she'd been preparing a delicious dinner: Would you like a drink?

Thanks.
Would you like to tell us about your building experiences?

Lina: Well, I'm a gopher.

Vic: She goes for this, she goes for that!

Lina: I stack the bricks – you know, get the bricks to him. And do anything that's necessary to help.

Vic: For that first house in Florida, she dry-mixed all the mortar for the bricks.

Lina: Oh, God!

Vic: She did the dry mix, and then I wet-mixed it. She mixed three-and-one.

Lina: With a hoe: you have a mud hoe.

Vic: It's a big hoe, steel, with three holes in it. You make yourself a trough, about six-foot long. We didn't want to layout in America for a concrete mixer on a one-off basis, so we did everything in a simplistic style. We minimized expenditure.

One of the difficulties in Britain is scaffolding. How did you manage for that?

Vic: Because of the cheap availability of lumber, I made up scaffolding, particularly for the gables. We built a posh brick house. We were the best in the area – so we were told.

Lina: I think that really we built better than the neighbourhood warranted. But then, if that's what you want to do, you do it.

Vic: The design was in keeping. The plot was 80′ wide, so we used the width. The depth was only 130′. We were in the early stages of the area being developed. Our house stood out. There were just trees to the left, and trees to the right. She looked impressive.

How had you come to settle there?

Vic: We had sailed through America.

Through America?

Vic: Yes; from South to North along the Intercoastal Waterway. Lina's sister came to meet us on the boat, in Florida. She and her husband liked the area, so eventually bought a place there. We built our houses near them, the roles reversed. Instead of us being the hosts, with our boat, they became local house-owners and hosted us.

You said that over there you buried the plumbing under the floor slab?

Vic: Yes. The copper pipes are planned to come up within the wall to distribute from there to whatever service is necessary. You have to fill the waste pipes with water, and you have to have a head of 8' to test it. The inspector comes, and it has to have water tipping over the top. He has to approve that before you pour the concrete.

The concrete contractor comes up with his ten-cubic-yard concrete mixer: they're running around banging it all down in ten minutes flat. The contractor gets the guys off the beach to do the spreading. He organizes the 5 ten-cubic-yard mixers. These guys are good with their chutes; they are 14' chutes. The spreaders are on three dollars an hour, or something. They're all friendly boys; they're all back on the beach after dinner.

Lina: As long as they've got plenty of beer!

Vic: Along comes another guy, and he polishes the edge for you with his trowel. They then polish with the float polisher – this is five o'clock the same day.

I tried a float polisher once, but didn't have much success with it. Is there a knack to it?

Vic: Yes; looks to me. But it's all part of the deal. You make your deal with the contractor, and you get a really polished surface. It's 37' by 64'. It's a big bungalow; the lounge was 40' long. You need the volume of air.

Lina: It's no good having doors. You'd suffocate.

It sounds that you used what we call a raft. You didn't use any trench foundation?

Vic: Only the edge. Where you're going to have load-bearing walls, you go down 18" and it's 18" wide. That's filled with concrete with reinforcing bar – twin reinforcing rods, $5/8$", on wire cage chairs so they were housed in a certain specific position. I think the prescribed depth up from the bottom was 3¹/₂".

You've got a membrane in there. You have to spray first for killer ants, termites. It has to be sequential: the man has to arrive with his high-powered chemical rubbish, get it all in there, then lay the membrane over the sprayed sand.

Lina: The Formosan termites eat the concrete! Or so we're told.

Vic: Your weld mesh is then put down and spaced, and the guys come and pour. There's no messing; they're expert. They don't want you anywhere near it. This was quarter to seven in the morning.

Over there, they have walk-in closets, wardrobes. In fact, we lived in one. In one corner, we built a walk-in closet, which was for the master bedroom, in the framework.

Lina: As big as an eight-by-four sheet of ply.

Vic: We lived in there, while we built it.

Was that considered a bit eccentric?

Vic: Yes. We got thrown out once by the police at midnight.

Lina: It was not really eccentric. It was time saving and labour saving. At the end of the day, we didn't want to drive fourteen miles back to my sister's. So I would cook a meal earlier on, then retire. Because we had no lights, we had to be off the site, so we'd just go to bed.

Vic: The closet was eight by four [feet] – a sheet of plywood. You see, you have snake problems.

The first one took nine months. That was full-time work for the two of us. We did everything. Charlie would come over from Orlando, one day a month. If I was putting up plasterboard on my own, I'd put up twelve sheets a day, working entirely on my own. Lina wasn't there then; I was entirely on my own. He'd come and help, and we'd be reduced to nine sheets a day with his help! Charlie wasn't a help; he meant well.

Lina: It doesn't pay to have friends' help. You talk more.

Vic: When they deliver the shingles [tiles] for the roof, they come on an X-frame truck, which goes up, and the guys just walk on and off the roof and leave them on the ridge.

The shingles are 3' by 1', with an overlap of about 3¹/₄". I laid mine on my own. Because the sun's shining everyday, you don't have to worry about anything. With chalk lines, I made all of mine square so it looked nice. A lot of people don't.

The roof is boarded with ¹/₂" board. Then it's sheathed with a tarry felt, then bituminized fibreglass shingles. With the sun, they bond to each other: the bitumen melts and they bond themselves.

Then the brick lorry comes with the bricks. He knows that Lina is going to be doing the labouring, so he helps her by driving his truck through the bushes and spotting the bricks all round for us.

Lina: I'm very fussy with my bricks. I don't like them all off one pile. I like to mix them up; if you don't, you can get patches. You see that on some houses – terrible.

Vic: In our first Florida house, when it came to caulking the joints of the plasterboard, prior to painting, I overdid it – there was far more sanding needed than necessary. Next time you do it, you know. You don't use nails, they use screws now. When you're banging a nail in there, you've got a half-crown to fill up. Now the modern trend is, with the battery operated screwdriver, to use these very cheap screws that you buy by the half hundredweight.

Lina: That's a tedious job—

Vic: —if you do it by the book, every six inches. They don't do it by the book, and with the screws, it's a much faster operation.

Lina: And they were very big rooms.

Is that true generally? There's a lot of space for American houses. Do they tend to be bigger than British ones?

Vic: In Florida, they are certainly bigger. They always have two or three bathrooms. Nobody would design a house without *en suite* in the master bedroom.

We had to be careful with snakes. There was a pygmy rattler. The bricks out there have three holes, and they get in the holes. They could kill you.

We designed and built the kitchen. The worktop is built of glazed tiles. We were trying to be a little different and make it saleable, and livable in fact. We lived in the place. We also made the furniture.

Did you turf the garden?

Vic: Yes. They deliver the sods on pallets. Lina lays them all.

Lina: You've got to do it, by law.

Vic: The front garden has to be done, the back you can get away with. They won't give you a certificate of occupancy until the lawn is laid, and trees put in. At least 15% of the bulldozed area has to be restored with trees, or trees retained from the original site—

Lina: —because in the beginning when we first went down there, they used to bulldoze the lot. Dreadful. They left just nothing.

Vic: We like decorative brickwork, not overpowering, but for a feature – a fireplace, or solid oak shelves with brick piers. Particularly, we like to have raked joints.

Lina: I always choose the bricks. I have pleasure in looking at the colours that I want, because they all vary. I take great pride in the brickwork, especially on the outside.

I don't do the bricklaying, I just mix the mortar. I have wanted to; I've watched Vic and I think I could. But when we're working, there's no time to piddle about.

Vic: You're always trying to achieve the most in the least time, in a straightforward way.

Lina: There's one thing I could never do, and that's to get the tiles onto the roof. We never had scaffolding; I found them heavy. That was the Redland Stonewold tiles.

Vic: At Levenheath, we had $16\frac{1}{2}$ tonnes.

Lina: I do all the painting. Victor doesn't like it.

We've been married nearly forty years now, and we're quite good friends now, on the whole. There are times when I disagree, but then it's better if I just keep quiet and let Victor get on with it. That happens if he's not sure himself what is going to happen. And then, instead of me querying it, I think it's better to leave him until he's sorted it out in his own mind. Then he discusses it; then we can talk about it.

Vic: It's true, I suppose – if the responsibility's mine eventually. Now, if we're hoisting a beam, a big steel lintel, and it's dangerous – now I've done it all my life, I've moved heavy objects skywards – I like to think it out quietly. I don't want somebody saying "Supposing we did this, supposing we put this bit of wood. . . ". I don't want to know about that. I want to quietly work it out; and then I'll say "Stand there; hold that rope; when I say 'pull', pull". You've got to think your own method through and then do it.

Lina: The trouble with me is that I cannot picture it from the measurements on the plan. I have to lay it out. Then if I find that the bathroom is too small, then Vic has to go in another direction.

To me, it always looks too small on the ground. Do you allow for that?

Vic: Yes; it always does. Rather than end up too small, I tend to end up too big.

Lina: Our bathroom at Levenheath, you could dance in it. But it was gorgeous. It was lovely for doing a few exercises, or something like that.

Vic: You can go into show houses in America, go into the bathroom and think "Yes, this is alright if it's three feet more".

Lina: The American houses are prettier. They seem to be more decorative; they have more features, internally particularly. People are looking for that. If you had a plain, solid house, it wouldn't be attractive.

Vic: They have many standardized fitments available. You couldn't think of something that they haven't already thought of and was available somewhere.

Lina: What I liked in one of our houses was that the dining area had a sunken floor – just a foot, but it made all the difference. It broke the line and made it very attractive.

Vic: It's now almost standard practice that you've got to incorporate a Jacussi. They don't turn me on.

Lina: They're nice; I like them. But I'd rather have a swimming pool!

Do you put in these features then?

Vic: If you're doing it for yourself, you do what you want. If you're thinking at some point of selling, then you really have to incorporate them.

Lina: If you build and you've got the ground, then do it.

Vic: – Because the cost is relatively small.

Lina: Afterwards it's much more difficult.
   The tiles, Brazilian and Mexican, are gorgeous.
   In Florida, everything is carpeted. I must say, I'd much rather have a wooden floor. In Maine, there will definitely be wooden floors. I've bought a beautiful Axminster carpet, and that's going to be a centre piece.

Do you think that you must have a strong relationship to work together and be together twenty-four hours a day?

Lina: Yes. In the boat we were together twenty-four hours a day. And we had a shop together. We've worked together for many a year now. One does the kissing and one holds the cheek. It's a 'give and take' thing.

Do you ever feel sorry about leaving your houses?

Vic: Slightly. You have to look at the plus side. They give you surplus cash, which allows you to move on, do another project, or have a holiday.

The house you're going to build in Maine looks huge.

Vic: No; big, not huge.

Lina: But it's not big for their standard.

Vic: Land is so expensive in Britain. Over there, we're talking of nothing, relatively speaking.
   We're fortunate that all the boundaries on our land are marked by stone that they've dug up over the centuries, and the boundary walls are

just stones (granite) thrown up – about six-foot wide and five-foot high. We'll use the stone for our walling.

And there's a timber mill half a mile down the road.

Lina: We're going to select our own trees and use them.

Vic: We've got between 100,000 and half a million trees on our land.

Lina: We'll never need fuel.

What about seasoning the timber? That's usually reckoned to take a year for an inch of thickness.

Vic: You've got to season it. You can kiln dry it. I wouldn't contemplate natural seasoning except for future furniture use.

We've got stands of ash, red oak, maple.

When we're at leisure, we can select and say "Yes; we'll have that one and season it". We'll rip it and season it.

Lina: There's one tree in the grounds, and to go round the circumference it needed four of us. It's so tall it's incredible. We're going to leave him standing. No way are we going to take him down.

Vic: I'm now going to draw the plans out from a picture in a book of plans. I always get ideas, and I maybe marry two or three different things and apply my own ideas.

Lina: The windows are troublesome.

Vic: Yes. I'm not prepared to have those windows made to my order down in ping-pong land and cost me about $10,000 to transport them up to Maine. Particularly as it's going to have to be double glazed, the handling of these big windows could be a little bit beyond my ability. There's a very upmarket window frame in America, Andersons, and I'll use those.

I get all the catalogues; that's bed-time reading for me.

The first level of this house is 2,300 square feet, the second only 930. By American standards, that's large but not huge.

We're not trying to impress anyone. We're just having an interesting project that will probably take us eighteen months to two years to get into a livable condition, and then perhaps, another three or four years for me to actually enjoy making furniture. You know, write letters to the Victoria and Albert museum and get leaflets back; just have a room with a theme, a furniture theme. I'm not going to do it all by hand. I'm going to use machinery, like my router and things like that. I'm going to do it to give me pleasure as well.

The windows that they offer as standard are expensive, but they're extremely cleverly thought out. They've got all sorts of possibilities, like nice, gentle bow windows. And we think that from that standard catalogue, taking this general idea, we can make it aesthetically pleasing to us, which is what matters. This is our house. We're not selling this.

I shall incorporate various solar features in it, solar panels and the like. The existing log house on the plot has solar panels. It also has a bio-loo. The vent from this, of warm air, goes through the auxiliary water heater. That's in the conservatory to use the sun's rays.

Lina: The space is attractive.

Vic: That's why we're going, really. Purely and simply – space.

Changing the subject rather, have you had any accidents while building?

Lina: The concrete mixer got to me one day.

Vic: She tried to stabilize it with a full mix going round and round, and it all fell on her.

Lina: It made a groove in my arm. Never again – just dive out of the way.

Is that the worst accident you've had?

Lina: Yes. No – Victor nearly lost his life.

How did that happen?

Vic: This is Levenheath and when we've got no money, and it's February, no more materials left, and the connection to the main drain is 250′ back and it's 15′ down. Right? So I've got to reach the 15′ down, which is in a farmer's field. I leave that part of it, and do all my arithmetic and graduate the 1 in 40, or whatever it was, down to the end of our garden, which I did.

It rained every bloody day while I dug the trench to the end of the garden. I kept bailing it out. Then I try to locate the Council's deep sewer. I find the manholes, and I sight through for a straight line. But Councils don't build in straight lines.

I start to dig by hand. The soil was stable, in the sense that twelve inches down and then you've got this glacial stone rubbish, and then you got hard clay. I was down 6′ to 8′ and throwing stuff up; and then I was down below where you can throw it up, so I've now got a vertical ladder up the side. I didn't shutter it. I was working steadily and minding my own business. I had a pulley up the top with two buckets. I would fill two buckets and climb up the ladder, pull the bucket out, chuck it on the heap, go down the ladder. A steady number. It was getting darkish, I was down 15′ and I hadn't found the bloody drain.

I was down this hole and a visitor, a policeman friend, came, and he said "I'll give you a hand, come on". So I began to work more quickly, trying to locate where this sewer could possibly be. I'd obviously reached the depth, and I hadn't found it.

I got up the ladder again, and thought "It's got to be that way". So I'm at the bottom of the hole, digging out the side, and I find the soft refill of the Council trench. It was immediately adjacent to my unshored hole. I just made it up the ladder. It got me all over the arms. It filled the whole bloody hole in. It collapsed on me. The whole bloody lot just caved in and came towards me.

– Only because we were hurrying. The policeman was saying "We've got to find it. Come on. I'll take that bucket; get it up". And it's getting softer dirt, and I thought "That's a bit odd". The Council had built in a curve.

Lina: If he hadn't have heard it. . .

Vic: It began. I thought "Christ!" – and I was up the ladder. But it got me all over the arms, even so.

Lina: . . .he would have gone.

Vic: I got out of there. It had filled that hole in. It took me another ten days. I shored it, of course.

Lina: So instead of a nice steady number, it was 'more haste less speed'. I was just thankful that he got out of it. If I had been there, I couldn't have done anything anyway.

Vic: Normally, I'm very careful. But this ground was so solid. And you kept pressing your luck, in the sense that there's not a movement in the top part.

How long did it take you to dig the first hole?

Vic: Ten days, I suppose. We went to an excavator to have it dug, but 15' down was pressing his luck a bit; he would have to go over the farmer's field and he'd destroy the early corn. Dick, the retired bricklayer next door, said "Oh, dig it boy. While you're talking about it, you could have got it dug". I had no money and no prospects, and I thought "Get on with it".

I dug towards this drain, ending up 10' down, with the last 5' as a drop. And that silly twit from the Council came round, the building inspector, to inspect it. And I said "It's your bloody fault there's not a tee on it". So 15' down, I had to cut a hole in their sewer.

Is it a difficult thing to do?

Vic: No. I had an angle grinder; I dished it out. But the Council had used a 6" drain instead of a 9" drain. They said it was a 9" drain. I had a 9" saddle to fit onto a 6" drain. It wasn't that far out; with some judicious concrete around it, two or three barrow-loads, it sat right. We poured some dyed water through, and looked down the far manhole, and it was alright.

Lina: That was a horrible year. When we dug the foundations, there was a drought. We dug three feet a day with a pickaxe. Then when we dug for the drain, it was the wettest February on record.

Vic: At that age, we'd done all our things, and our sailing, and our boat building, and all those other previous things with houses and that, and suddenly we'd got to start again financially because of all the hyperinflation. This was '76.

Lina: I was getting a bit fed up with it by that time. We lived in a caravan, and I worked in Boots three days a week and had to keep myself nice.

We'd had everything before, but lost it all going sailing.

Vic: We were starting again. It's a bit depressing when you're 47 years old.

Have you got some enthusiasm for your next house?

Lina: Yes. We don't have to hurry. We've got a nice home to live in. [There is already a log house on their plot of land.] It's not like in a caravan, where it can be very hot, it can be very cold.

Vic: Yes; this is 'civilized living' we're going to.

Lina: We shall see. If we're not too old for it.

Vic: If I moved that boat the other month, I'm not too old. [Vic had recently been involved in building a large catamaran.]

I moved that 60' catamaran out of that shed, using my chain hoist horizontally. We had to turn it in a distance it wouldn't turn in basically. We had to shunt the front across and the back across. Can you imagine shunting a 60' by 24' object? We had some rollers for moving industrial machinery. Of course, the floors were all sorts of levels, so there were three rollers on and one not. It was quite an interesting two to three days.

But I hurt my back. That was the first time I've hurt my back in my life. It's still there.

Lina: It's too late now; it's damaged. Which is very sad really, because he's never been anything else but well – and trying to do this, two men doing six men's job. Ridiculous.

Vic: I suddenly became in charge of it, by nobody else being there. And it had got to be done. Nobody had made any arrangements. I could have punched somebody in the head, but I thought "No, I've seen it this far, I'm going to see it through".

If I could move that boat, I can build a piddly, little thing like a house!

5

STAN
BURT

THE PROFESSIONAL BUILDER WHOSE WORK IS
HIS HOBBY

STAN BURT is a professional builder with a difference. I first came across him on the Isle of Wight where he was building a house to retire to. For family reasons, that didn't happen and the house was sold. The buyer had it surveyed, and the surveyor's conclusion was that you could travel the length of the land and not find such a well built house. Characteristically, Stan Burt himself is more modest, saying that there is always room for improvement. Be that as it may, the house had been built immaculately. And it was all his own work; he built the entire house unaided. Moreover, he disdains machinery. And so, although the house was built on a hillside with the result that a lot of excavating was needed for the foundations, all was dug out with pick and shovel.

There is a characteristic that all builders need, and that is persistence. Stan Burt shows plenty of this, whether digging into hillsides or fighting Government bureaucracies. (His struggle for his right to build his own house was even discussed in the House of Commons.)

I interviewed Stan Burt in Surrey, in the bungalow he had built some time after the Second World War. Needless to say, that too was immaculate, with a lot of special features. As it happened, he and his wife were just about to sell it and move to the Isle of Wight – to an old cottage!

We talked about the bungalow he had built all those years ago and was just about to leave, and about the house he had built recently in Ventnor, the Isle of Wight.

☆   ☆   ☆   ☆   ☆

When did you build this bungalow that you're soon to be leaving?

Stan Burt: '49 to '53. I had restrictions; I wasn't allowed to build it. Government restrictions stopped me. [In post-War Britain, the supply and use of materials was strictly controlled.] So I built it spare time. They even tried to stop me building it spare time, although I could get the materials. I wasn't allowed to use the materials in my own time. There were licences at that time, and they were limited.

Everything was OK, Planning, bye-laws, but I couldn't put it together. I could have the materials on the site, but I wasn't allowed to assemble it in my own free time. It was absolutely crazy. They threatened me with court cases and that sort of thing. It went up to the House of Commons.

During a year, you could do a hundred pounds worth of work on property, but no more. So what I did, I put the foundations in, I put the sewer in, I put the slab over, and I called that a hundred pounds. In the meantime, unbeknown to them, I made all the window frames, because they were all hand-made on the job. I made them and everything I could in the shed outside.

The next hundred pounds worth was due to start July 1st. It was such lovely weather that I started a week before time. And they came up and and saw I'd started. Then they threatened me. They took it to a special committee of the Council – they decided to let it go this time, but they wouldn't take a tolerant view in future. Then I got up to roof height for the next hundred pounds. *Laughter.* I got the plate on.

All the time, I was trying to get a licence, and they wouldn't grant it because we weren't married. To cut a long story short, we decided to get married and arranged a date. This is 1951. We made an application to get a special licence to use the materials in my own spare time. The day before the wedding, the Council wrote that the Ministry of Housing would grant us a licence, and hoped it would increase our happiness on this happy occasion.

I'd fought them every time. I'd told them they could take me to court, they could give me six months, they could give me two years; and I said I'd come out and I'd fight again. I was fighting for common sense. But it was absolutely crazy. I've still got Hansard's report with it in.

Was it plain sailing after you'd got the licence?

Stan Burt: I wasn't allowed to employ anybody, which I didn't want to do anyhow. I had to do it completely on my own. So I did the whole thing.

What were you doing in the meantime?

Stan Burt: I was working for myself then. I was self-employed, building. I was doing a full-time job and coming here at half-five, having my tea up here, and then I'd carry on. I worked winter. It didn't matter what the time was – I floodlit it.

Was it unusual for people to build their own houses in those days?

Stan Burt: There was some selfbuild, but I think that mostly came afterwards. There wasn't a lot of it done. At this time, there were so many restrictions that you couldn't.

Do you mind me asking how old you were at the time?

Stan Burt: Well, I'm 68 now; I was born in 1920 – thirty I suppose.

I started in partnership with a friend, at 26 actually. We built his house spare time first – he was married and had a licence. I'd been doing all trades for a long time.

Stan Burt's bungalow in Surrey

Had you had any training in any of them?

Stan Burt: Self-taught. I'm a carpenter and joiner by trade. I've got City and Guilds in that. I went to evening classes for it.

During the War, I was on aerodrome construction. In '46, I took a temporary job until we could go on our own. I've always been in construction. I trained myself in various trades because I've always been interested. You can do a lot of things if you're practical and can use your hands.

Which are the trades which you find the most difficulty with?

Stan Burt: No; it's not difficulty; it's things I don't like doing. Plastering, for instance – I don't enjoy that at all, it's too dirty, it's much of a muchness. Carpentry and joinery is definitely the first because there is so much variety. You get more pleasure from it.

On the house on the Isle of Wight, for example, I made the staircase from sawn timber. I planed it all by hand on an improvised bench. I didn't want machining to lose the thickness. It was very rewarding.

This bungalow was the main project for myself. I've learnt a lot of things since. As I say, all the external doors and windows I made on site.

You made the doors?

Stan Burt: Oh, yes.

I don't suppose you had many power tools in those days?

Stan Burt: I never have used power tools. The only thing I ever use now is a drill, an electric drill. No; it was all hand-mortised, everything.

How do you feel about leaving it all behind now, now that you're about to move to the Isle of Wight?

Stan Burt: I've got used to the idea, I suppose. My son has gone to the Island. If it wasn't for him, I suppose we'd have stayed here.

We've found something that we like, now, to move to. It's a 150-year-old cottage. It's got a bit of character to it.

Is your son a builder?

Stan Burt: No; he's never been interested. That's the disappointing thing.

How many houses have you been involved in building?

Stan Burt: I did the bungalow next door, and the one up the road. I've done about twelve I suppose, myself; not everything myself, but most of it.

One time my brother was with me as well. He's been on his own; he's just coming up to retirement now. He's built a few more than I have. I trained him in the trade. He can adapt himself to more or less all things as well. It's more of a business for him. To me, while it was a job of work, it was also a hobby. So I got the pleasure out of doing it. I didn't look at the pounds, shillings and pence.

I imagine you did well enough though, didn't you?

Stan Burt: Oh, yes; I suppose. But I never made fortunes on building. I never intended to. I made a living.

The plot at Ventnor was on a hillside. Was it difficult to build on?

Stan Burt: Yes. About 250 tonnes of aggregate has gone in there, in the foundations and the drive.

I dug it all out myself. I don't like machines, you see. The only machine that had to come in was to prepare the drive. Because there was so much material there to be moved, I got a caterpillar bulldozer-excavator in to do it. That's all.

Did you use readymixed concrete?

Stan Burt: No. I did have a little electric mixer there, for the first time. For this bungalow and everything up to then, everything I did by hand-mixing till I bought this little machine. Though to be strictly accurate, I had once before used a colleague's mixer.

Do you know what the surveyor told the present owner of your Ventnor house before the purchase? – He said that you'd have to travel the length of the country to find a house as well built as that one.

Stan Burt: That's his own view, not mine. But perhaps I did overdo it. There was a satisfaction there, because it was from drawing board to finished product. I designed it. Nobody else has had anything to do with it at all.

How long did it take to build?

Stan Burt: It's hard to say because I used to do other bits and pieces. It went over for a fair time, three years I suppose.

Did you make the windows for this one too?

Stan Burt: No; that I didn't do. They were Boulton and Paul's 'High Performance'. The only joinery I made there was the staircase and external door frames.

How many bedrooms does it have?

Stan Burt: Three. It's got three large bedrooms. We could have had more, but we built to what suited ourselves, not to what you could put on the plot.

There is a kind of cellar?

Stan Burt: Yes – underneath the entrance, with a bedroom above actually. As you came in the front door, there was a hallway and then a bedroom; then you went down to the living room and up to the bedrooms. There was a lot of excavation, a terrific amount. And I used it all up for forming the contours of the land. I never took anything away: it was all used. It was all done with pick and shovel.

But you had electric power into your caravan, did you?

Stan Burt: Yes; and I had a socket for plugging into for outside use.

How did you get on, not driving a vehicle?

Stan Burt: All materials were delivered to the site. For a very occasional thing, I'd go down into town. But I wouldn't like to try it again, not like that. There wasn't a phone on site, so I had to go to the phone box.

I called myself 'semi-retired' when I was doing it. Sometimes I'd come back here [to the bungalow in Surrey] and paint the outside up. I had to maintain this place and my son's place.

Is there any kind of advice you'd like to give to other people about selfbuild?

Stan Burt: I can't think of any advice; not really. It's a challenge. As I say, if you're practical, if you're enthusiastic, you've got to be willing and keen to do it – because it was a hobby as well as a job of work, you see. Going back, when I was a youngster working for somebody else, I couldn't wait for the next day to come; I wanted to get back cracking, doing something. I enjoyed it so much; it was a part of me. That was the best part of the week. I was waiting for the next morning to come to start again. *Laughter.*

It sounds as though you're still as enthusiastic.

Stan Burt: Well, no. I've lost a lot of it actually, the enthusiasm – because you've got nothing to drive for, you haven't any career to form, you haven't got to work for anything. You've either achieved something or you haven't achieved it, and you come to the end of your working life. You realize that you've got to put your tools down in the end, so you lose all the enthusiasm and drive that you did have. It's unfortunate, but so are a lot of things. I suppose you haven't got either the energy or the zest.

If my son had been in the trade, that'd be something to work for.

Did you have any trouble selling the Ventnor house?

Stan Burt: I had a NHBC certificate for it. I was a member of the council for that very reason. I became great friends with their field officer – only through my construction and what I've done, there was no conniving between us.

Was he impressed, compared to everything else he had to look at?

Stan Burt: Yes; he was. He bought one of his superiors to show him. We're great friends. We've stayed in contact ever since.

The NHBC is really due to come every three weeks, where of course, the Council's building inspector only comes on certain definite stages: excavations, foundations, drains, damp course and things.

How did you get on with building inspectors?

Stan Burt: Oh, I got on very well. No problems at all.

It depends what quality you do, I suppose.

If you're trying to pull a fast one over them, you're forever in trouble, you could be. Do everything right, and that's it.

What about the drains of the Ventnor house?

Stan Burt: There was a septic tank, one of those big plastic things. I dug the hole for that as well. I struck plenty of rock.

Stan Burt's house on a hillside

It's not chalk?

Stan Burt: No; it's mostly rock. There's a good solid rock base there. The foundation is really in rock. It's a good foundation, no problem whatsoever.

Did you know that a lot of Ventnor is slipping?

Stan Burt: Yes – but this is on the right side of Ventnor. It's not where the landslip is. A lot of insurance companies won't insure property there.

How do you find electrics?

Stan Burt: I have to think on it, but I enjoy doing it. Especially at the Ventnor house. I've got the cylinder on one motorized valve, I've got valves on the two floors – I've got valves on each of those. And then there had to be a relay in there to control the switching so that things didn't get overloaded. So I had problems with the relaying – not problems, but just sorting it out everywhere. I designed the system.

How do you keep up with the technology?

Stan Burt: I got details of the thermostats and that from the makers. The valves have been in use quite a time now. They're very effective. They automatically open and shut. But it all had to be done with a relay. Even an electrician couldn't sort it out. I took it to an electrician, and he couldn't sort out which connections to make; so I sorted it out in the end myself.

What does the relay do?

Stan Burt: It switches over from one valve to another. If you had all three open at the same time, the system would be overloaded; so it's done in sequence with the relay. It worked alright. I was quite pleased.

Did you use double glazing?

Stan Burt: Yes. They were sealed units. But I had some faults with them. The seal broke down on a number of occasions. One or two went beyond the guarantee, but the company replaced them free. There was a fault somewhere along the line. They were guaranteed five years. It was only the tiny ones that went first, and then it got to a larger one. Yet it was a well known make; it had all the stamps, BSS or whatever.

When one goes, you get clouding. Moisture gets in there and then it can't get out. You couldn't see anything wrong with them.

Is there insulation in the walls?

Stan Burt: No; they wouldn't allow me to do it. I wanted to do it, but they said it was too exposed. Now they might allow it.

But it is dry lined in there. It's quite complicated putting it up, but you can make a lovely job of it. You can get a super finish if you put the pads up right. You put pads on and level them off with a straight edge first. Then you put on plaster dabs, long ones. They come forward of the pads, so that when you push the board back you pick up those pads. You've got a super job then, if you do it right. Of course, you've got to tape the joints properly, otherwise you'll finish up with imperfections.

Does it take as long as plastering?

Stan Burt: I should think it takes as long as plastering, nearly; it wouldn't take longer. All external angles I use are metal; they make a super job.

Is it a fiddly job, filling the joints in?

Stan Burt: Yes; you've got to use two different types of material. I don't know if they've altered it since. [Yes; they have. Only one material is now required: Gyproc Jointex.] There's one for building it up and putting the tapes in, and another for the actual finish. It's quite intricate. I'd never done it before. It's a messy job, but then plastering's a messy job. You get a really true finish.

They're tapered edge boards. There's a slight sinking at the edge, sufficient to tape it without coming proud.

How did you finish them?

Stan Burt: I sealed them to seal the paper surface of the board so you don't damage it in future, and I emulsioned it so it gives a good base for future decoration. If you papered it direct, when you come to strip off, you might get down to the plasterboard itself.

How did you finish the ceilings?

Stan Burt: They were artexed. I did that. I think artex is better actually; there's no problems with cracking. I only use a very fine stipple, nothing heavy. I don't like some of these heavy finishes.

What bricks did you use?

Stan Burt: They came from Sussex. They were sand-faced stocks. We wanted something different. I liked them.

In the cellar I used concrete blocks, and lightweight ones above it.

What about the tiles?

Stan Burt: They're only a concrete tile, interlocking. They're a nice tile, actually – if there is anything nice about a concrete tile.

People building their own house find that scaffolding is a problem because they have it up so long. How did you manage?

Stan Burt: I owned it myself. I put my own scaffolding up. Then I sold it at the end. I realized I wasn't going to do it again.

Most builders don't put their own scaffolding up now. It's erected by scaffolders, for insurance purposes – accidents, that sort of thing. You've got to have these safety guards, toe guards, that sort of thing.

What mortar did you use?

Stan Burt: The mortar? – I used sand-and-cement with Febmix in. I always used to use lime and sand and cement. You used to knock it up and leave it for quite a time before you added the cement to it. It's a good thing. It's not like the old lump lime they used to use, which you had to slake down before you could use it. That bubbled and boiled. They had to do that before they could make mortar or plaster then.

But ordinary lime you mix with sand, and you can leave it quite a time – weeks – provided that it doesn't get too dry with the sun, or anything. It gets more fatty. It's not too sharp. Then add cement to that as you want it.

Is there head height in the cellars under the floors?

Stan Burt: Not head height: you've got to crawl down, more or less.

The plumbing and electrics are all accessible there. I did all the central heating from underneath. It was a bit awkward, mind you.

Wouldn't it have been easier to put it in before you put the floor-boards down?

Stan Burt: I didn't like that. I wanted it so that you could do anything with it afterwards. Everything's accessible. You can get at it after-wards, if you want to, without any problem.

The floors are floor-boards; I don't like chipboard. All the floor-boards they sent me were white deal, and I sent the lot back. They bought me red deal floor-boards then. I polished them all, actually. The floors were waxed right through. They were tongue-and-grooved. It's a smashing floor. While I was doing the artexing and while I was doing the plastering, they were all upside down, so it didn't mess the floor-boards up. Then, when I fixed them, I reversed the boards so you got a clean surface. By that time, they were seasoned and everything, so you didn't get shrinkage cracks.

That's an advantage of taking your time.

Stan Burt: Well, of course, years ago, before my time mostly, timber was seasoned like that on the job. Nothing was built in a hurry.

On this house, all the timber was pressurized. Every floor-board was pressurized. It went in for vac-vac treatment. Otherwise it was heavily brushed, so that it was absorbing it and absorbing it until it wouldn't absorb any more. The whole lot in the property was treated.

Did you paint the frames?

Stan Burt: When they were well seasoned. You shouldn't seal moisture in. I used primer and two undercoats, sometimes three. And of course, the art is rubbing down between coats, too. It's like the finish they got a long time ago. You get a finish that you feel is reasonable, without showing the grain of the wood too much and things like that. Two topcoats quite often.

So you usually had two undercoats and two top coats?

Stan Burt: Quite often. Sometimes, with primer, it would be six coats in some cases. I quite often do two coats of gloss, but I like to build the base up of undercoat, which may be two or three coats. It depends if it doesn't cover or anything.

Is that for inside as well?

Stan Burt: On the inside, it would always be two undercoats. Undercoat's most important to get the base.

You said you sent back some white deal. Why is red deal much better than white deal?

Stan Burt: Because of the natural resins. You can tell the red deal by the red knots; the wood looks red – although we used to call it yellow deal years ago. White deal they used to use only for scaffold boards and the cheaper sort of structural timbers: roof timbers and things like that. It twists like mad sometimes.

That's the trouble with the rot. Now, things are pressurized. But in the Sixties, virtually nothing was treated, and it was inferior, and rot's rampant in a lot of cases, especially barge boards and things like that. Red deal's got natural resins, so moisture doesn't penetrate so well.

Did you use roof trusses?

Stan Burt: The apex has roof trusses; they wanted that. Otherwise, they wanted calculations – a load of nonsense. So I have got roof trusses. But I increased the size of the timbers. I wouldn't have them the ordinary thickness; I wanted them to go up an inch, so they're thicker than normal. And they're all at 16″ centres; they're not 2′ apart like they put them nowadays.

But other parts of the roof use heavier timbers. There's nine-by-three [inch] purlins in there, and things like that. They wanted them in there. You can see the roof line is broken. I wanted that; I didn't want a straight slope.

In the hall, I've got a curved ceiling onto the landing at the top. It's in matchboard. It looks very effective, actually. I selected every length in the timber merchants, and then I had it pressurized.

You had that treated?

Stan Burt: Everything's done; yes. Stairs, skirting, everything I had is pressurized.

The floors are all treated with preservative. Then I sealed them, and then they're all wax polished.

All done by hand?

Stan Burt: All done by hand.

I've got a shelf all the way round the bath. It only wants one leg for the bath, just to keep the balance there, because the rest is supported on all that timber frame. Nothing'll ever move there; you'll never get a crack round the bath, or anything like that.

It's a cast-iron basin, the same type as the bath, made by the same people.

What size skirting did you use?

Stan Burt: Five inch; I didn't go down to the smallest size. Some of them are only a means of closing the gap up between the floor and the plastering.

The window boards are parana pine; I left them natural. It looks very effective.

You must have been putting in quite a few hours a week?

Stan Burt: Oh, yes – building and landscaping.

There's 50 tonnes of concrete in the drive, besides all the hardcore that's underneath it. I mixed it all myself and laid it all myself. It's a good solid drive.

I used shuttering to support the concrete terrace. The only thing that worried me, when you've got a big bay to do and it's all reinforced concrete, was the thought "If the mixer packs up, what do I do?". But anyway, nothing went wrong, it worked alright. The mixer was very good actually. It was only a little one. I've still got it, as clean as the day I bought it nearly.

Did you seed the lawn?

Stan Burt: Yes; it's all seeded.

I don't suppose you used a rotavator, did you?

Stan Burt: No, no. I dug it over. It's been turned over about three times. I got it weed free. Then I used about two hundredweight of grass seed.

These days, there's very few people with your attitude to building.

Stan Burt: Well, I suppose I'm a bit different!

6

DAVE AND
BARBARA

AN EASY-TO-BUILD HOUSE IN THE SEGAL STYLE

THE ARCHITECT, WALTER SEGAL, developed a system of easy house construction, especially suitable for selfbuild. The system eliminates the wet trades, bricklaying and plastering; the foundations are based on concrete piles, saving vast amounts of excavating and concreting; and the roof is flat, avoiding tiling and any complex timber construction. Instead, timber frames stand on the concrete piles, and the walls and roof are built up from sheet materials, in particular wood-wool slabs. Designs are based on a modular grid, compatible with the manufactured sizes of the sheets, so reducing the need to cut the sheet materials.

The method was taken up by the Lewisham Local Authority in London. They sponsored a small selfbuild housing association that built eight bungalows in the mid-Seventies. In the mid-Eighties, they followed that up with a somewhat larger scheme of thirteen houses. These were built on a woody sloping site where the foundations for conventional houses would have been difficult, and the silvan nature of the site lost. One of the advantages of the Segal method is that it can tolerate trees close to the foundations.

The participants in the scheme were either living in Council houses or were on the waiting list. Although this was a group scheme, individuals basically built their own houses. Dave, a market trader, and Barbara, a teacher, were one of the couples involved.

☆   ☆   ☆   ☆   ☆

How did you get involved in this project?

Dave: It was through a friend of ours who, back in '79, did a video of the first scheme. What he told us about it, we thought "Oh, wonderful; that sounds great". So he said to us "Why don't you put your name down?". We thought "What's to lose? We're in a Council flat, with two children. How else do we actually get into a house of our own?".

Barbara: – In London? As a first-time buyer?

The scheme was organized by the local Council, Lewisham?

Dave: Yes. Lewisham did the first scheme. That was a way to give families who were on the Council waiting list an opportunity to build their own house.

It works out cost effective because the Council get houses built, good structural houses that are guaranteed to last for a minimum of fifty years, and they get people who are on their waiting list off into the private market. They've got additional rate payers. They've got land that was vacant being productive, in the sense that it's providing cheap family dwellings. All round, everybody wins. And at a very low cost.

And you end up with your own house?

Dave: Yes.

At the time, we never thought it would actually come off. It all sounded so nice on paper. It was just an idea, almost like a Utopia – we could be happy, the Council could be happy, everybody could be happy.

Barbara: But what got us really going was when we went to see Johnny Broom's house, the architect who was working with the Council. He lived in a selfbuild bungalow on the first scheme. His bungalow – I just fell in love with it. That's when I started to get excited.

How much money did you have to find yourselves to do it?

Dave: We didn't have to find anything.

Barbara: Literally, none. The Council bought your tools, and we had communal tools to share on site. In the eventuality, we did buy a few tools. We got sick of sharing power tools, which is all very nice in theory. It obviously makes sense if people are willing to share. But in the end, if your time is precious, and if you can't get hold of a tool, or it's got lost . . . In the end, it was back to our own selfish, little ways.

Do you now own the house and have a mortgage on it?

Barbara: We haven't actually got our mortgage yet. On the first scheme, it took four years from completion to actually receiving their mortgages. We're in our second year.

So are you paying the Council rent at the moment?

Dave: Yes. On the first scheme, they were paying half rent until they got their mortgages. We're assessed on £24 a week, plus rates. We're paying £12 a week, plus rates.

Barbara: – Joke!

What's going to happen when you go over to a mortgage?

Barbara: We won't be able to afford four weeks in St Lucia [in the West Indies]! It's going to be a bigger chunk out of our money. The price is fixed, so even if we don't get our mortgage for another five years, it's going to be exactly the same then as it is now.

Dave: The final accounting is £33,000 to £35,000 a house, depending on what you've done to your house.

Is that the price you buy it at?

Dave: Yes. Though each house is allocated £7,000 labour costs, which is to be deducted from the total figure.

Does that include the land?

Dave: Not initially. What they're doing is selling the freehold of the whole site to the Lewisham Self-Build Housing Association Phase II. We're all members of the Housing Association. And then we ourselves can sell to individual members the freehold of the individual plots at a nominal fee.

When you have bought the freehold from the housing association, will the house be yours like any other house?

Dave: Yes. What we've done, though, to maintain the character of the place, we've agreed that as a housing association, you've got to nominate someone to come in and buy your place. And they would have to be approved by the group. We don't see that causing any problem. From the first scheme, no-one's actually sold, and this is ten years on.

So they're quite happy where they are?

Dave: Well, it's two-and-a-half years of work, constantly just living, breathing, sleeping, eating the whole thing. When you've done that kind of sacrifice, it's become almost part of you.

Is that two-and-a-half years of building, or is some of that the planning?

Dave: No; that's just how long it took to build our house. It took four years from the inception of this second scheme for it to get started. We ourselves spent six months to a year going to meetings.

Barbara: We came into the scheme late.

Dave: We came in at the end of it. The people at the beginning were tied up with it for four years until they actually got a spade in their hands.

Even when we were going to meetings, in the back of my mind I was thinking "Is it really going to come off?". It was like a front I was putting on. The reason that we got a place was that people on the waiting list dropped out.

How many houses are there in the project?

Dave: We've a combination on the estate of five couples with children, a senior woman, a senior man and wife, a separated man, three man-and-woman, a separated mother with a child, and a single man.

That's thirteen.

Barbara: One guy split from his wife during building. It's hard to say if it was because of the building. Maybe in the normal run of things you can paper over the cracks for a lot longer, but with building you can't. If you're not getting on, you can't hide it.

Dave: I think that you've got to have it in your mind, as a couple, that if you're entering into this sort of thing there's going to be a period in your life when things are going to be really difficult. You've just got to be a bit more understanding.

There are two special features to this scheme. One is the way the Council sponsored it, but the other one is the Walter Segal method of building.

Barbara: Yes. It's not in a pre-made kit as people like to ask – "Did it all come in kit form?".

What is the basis of the Segal method?

Dave: His whole philosophy behind it was to help people create their own homes.

Barbara: I think that one of the main points is that the foundations are so simple. This land is very sloping, but they allow the houses to be put up without too great a problem. And it's just building simplified really, cutting out all the wet skills – bricklaying, plastering – which, if you haven't done it before, you'll find difficult. And none of the carpentry was that complicated really. And the drawings are simplified.

What were the foundations?

Dave: The house itself stands on twelve legs, and then you put on an additional two for verandas or porches. All it is, is a pile for each leg. On a conventional house, over the whole area where the house is going to be erected, you have it concreted over – a great, big concrete slab. With these, you don't have to do a complete concrete slab. You just bore holes, spaced out according to the plan, four metres deep, 12″ diameter, and concrete is poured into them with reinforcement.

Did you have the holes bored by machine?

Dave: Yes. We hired contractors who came in with a boring machine. They bored the twelve or fourteen holes and poured reinforced concrete into them. The ground wasn't level; it wasn't completely cleared of brambles or whatever. When they'd done it, all you saw was these wires sticking up. At these points, you've got to build some shuttering, pour your concrete into it, and put a paving stone on top. Then you've got to fill the whole plan area with paving stones. They might be just bedded onto sand and ballast. Of course, you know which are the twelve fixed ones. You don't actually have to level the land at all. It could flow in any direction, as long as the paved area has a slight camber so that water can run off.

It must have been very quick to make these foundations.

Dave: Oh, yes. The contractors came in, and in a day, they did maybe four houses. When ours was done, we started clearing the bramble away and getting ready to put the paving stones down. I didn't like that part of the work at all. And yet we had it easy, because on the first scheme they had to manually dig the holes. It takes a long time to dig one hole, and if you had rain in between, it would fill up, so you couldn't pour concrete into that hole. If you've got to go four metres down – that's quite a depth. And a narrow hole – it's even more dangerous.

Barbara: How did they do it?

Dave: They got down in the hole, and got bucketfuls, and raised the bucket above their head and out. They had to build bigger holes because of the fact that they were going down there. One guy going down met an old motor scooter. So there was all this clay coming out, and it took them weeks to do the foundation work. At the end of it, they bought in some machinery.

So you learnt from their experience?

Dave: Yes. We were told we were total softies because we'd got this contractor to do the hard bit. There was a little bit of rivalry there with the first group. Another problem they had was storage of materials. They had a lot of material come down to be stored, and pieces would go missing or be hard to locate.

So what did you do?

Dave: We still stored some, but we kept it down to a minimum. So we ordered a week in advance of when we needed it.

Barbara: Each plot ordered individually. So when we knew we were going to be doing our floor, we put an order in for our floor-boards, rather than have the floor-boards sitting there from the beginning.

How was everything being organized as a group? Did you go to meetings and say "We'll be wanting some floor-boards in a couple of week's time", and then everybody worked out together what was needed to be ordered?

Dave: The Council had a co-ordinator, Beverley. She was part of the group, but she wasn't a builder. She was paid. She was the person who dealt with the suppliers: she'd call them up on the phone and place the orders, and keep the accounts. She handled the cheques.

The Council sent her the cheques in £20,000 lots, which she deposited. Through Beverley we did all our ordering. We'd call her up and say "I'm ready for this"; and she would try and co-ordinate it. When she called up the timber company, she wouldn't just order the floor-boards for one plot; she would try and wait until there was two, three or maybe four ready for the floor-boards. There was always something else you could get on with.

Once you'd started building, were you still having meetings?

Barbara: Yes; we were. We were sorting out arguments. Deliveries were on Saturday morning. At first, everybody was supposed to be there for deliveries, but that wasn't practical. Then it got to be so that some people were always spending their Saturday mornings unloading. Everybody's time is precious. So then we had to work out a rota.

If Dave and me were in charge of delivery one Saturday morning, we'd find out what was coming. And then we'd phone round to make sure we had enough people there to help us, particularly the people whose orders were coming in.

Dave: There was that kind of responsibility to see that everybody took a fair whack of the general duties. At the initial start of the project, we had to make sure that all the perimeter fencing was erected. So as a group we got into that. There were times when it got fraught, and people were arguing about: 'I've been doing this and this for so many weeks, and you haven't done that' – that kind of thing. But it wasn't something that I would play on; disagreements are natural. There were thirteen people, different persuasions, different ideas of how things have got to be done. They had different responsibilities themselves. We were raising two children. We had to arrange our life around the fact that we were now house builders, as well as parents.

Was that difficult?

Dave: Well, we knew we had to make some sacrifices. Basically, our sacrifices were our social life. It was non-existent for two-and-a-half years. If somebody offered to take the kids off our hands for a day, we thought "Right, we can really get stuck in up on the site". It wasn't "Right, we can go off to the pictures", or something like that.

I know that we used it to actually solidify our relationship.

Barbara: To cement it!

It can lead to relationships splitting up.

Barbara: It either makes or breaks.

Dave: At first, I was very, very. . . I don't know –

Barbara: – a bossy pig.

Dave: I was a bossy bastard.

A male, chauvenist pig?

Barbara: They were all male chauvenists up here.

It was always to the women: "Go and make us a cup of tea, will you?".

With the foundations there, what happened next?

Dave: With the foundations done, we had delivery for the framing.

The architect and his assistant wrote out a plan of action, of what they expected you to achieve by a certain time.

Was this Walter Segal himself?

Dave: Yes; it was.

It was basically: clear the land, do the perimeter fencing, then work on foundations, and then do the framing. The framing would progress to the joisting. The roof would come at the end of the first bit of joisting, because you wanted to get some kind of cover. After the joisting, you'd start putting in your utilities like your electric wiring and plumbing. Then it was floor-boards; and then you'd put up the walls and then windows.

Do you remember how long it took to get the roof on from the foundations being done?

Barbara: The first winter we were clearing the site and doing the foundations. The second winter, when it struck hard, we'd just got our roof on and some walling up as winter was coming.

Dave: The foundations were quite a long period, or it seemed long because I hated it.

Each pile had to be shuttered, and 130 paving slabs laid over the plan area, on a bed of sand and ballast.

Barbara: The frame went up in the summer.

Dave: Each house consisted of four frames. A frame consisted of three legs – three posts if you like – connected by three beams. The two central frames have double beams running across the three posts: there's a double beam for the ground floor, for the first floor, and for the roof. So the double beams sandwich these posts together. You've got three legs, so there's nine pieces of wood in one frame – that's the two central frames. The outer frames have three posts having single beams, so they'll have six pieces. We were using high quality timber – Douglas fir.

Having built the frames on the flat, you need a good group of people to get them into place. You need about a dozen people to move a frame without twisting it and distorting it.

Do you really need so many? For an individual selfbuilder using the Segal method, it would be difficult to find so many people.

Dave: Maybe not so many were needed, but the more there were the less the stress, the less the chance of twisting the frames unduly. The frame raising was an event which we were all nervous about, and the numbers reflected the level of intensity.

Anyway, basically you were working on your own house, but occasionally, when you needed it, other people would help?

Dave: Yes. Working on your own house meant getting the work ready, so that, when you did need a group of people to put the work into place, you could call on them. That's one of the things I found that was bad. Some people would call you and have you twiddling your thumbs. It could be so infuriating; they weren't quite ready for you. I had a few arguments about that.

Barbara: It was very exciting when the first frames went up. They go up so quick; it's only a couple of hours. It suddenly becomes three dimensional. You'd been working on this two dimensional level on the ground, building the frames on the flat, then suddenly you can see your space.

What's keeping the frames in position?

Barbara: You've got to joist them out quick. They're only held up, temporarily, with bits of wood like scaffolding around them, or by securing a bit of wood to a tree.

Dave: You set the spaces between each frame – you use two-by-two [inch] wood to space the gaps out, and this determines the joist lengths. You try and square up the frames as much as you possibly can before you start cutting your joists to go in place. Start with the ground-floor joists, work to the first floor, and then the roof.

So there's no scaffolding on the outside?

Dave: No. Basically, you're clambering over these frames. I thought it was alright, because once you started joisting you started putting boards down so that you could walk across. It was really nice, because you started rising up off the ground, and you were up on the first floor, and then you reached the roof. And then it was like "Yeah, it's really coming together".

You're on the ground working on these frames for such a length of time that you can't even think about the point where you're off the ground. It's a funny concept. It's like you've transcended to being almost super-powerful, because here you are fiddling around with these tools on the ground level, and when you raise this thing up, it's so many feet higher than your physical body. It's a kind of a nice feeling to get to that point.

Barbara: There are definite stages, high points. Ninety percent of it is just slog, boring slog, where you hardly seem to see what you're doing. But then there are those lovely moments, when a definite stage is finished, when you see something complete.

Dave and Barbara's Segal-style house

Dave: Every part of the job, no matter how monotonous it was and repetitive, when it was done, it was a sense of real achievement.

With wood, when it's stained and varnished, it looks nice. It might have been rough when it was on the ground, but when you put the stain on, the wood takes on a kind of character. We could look at it and say "Oh, look at the fine lines in it", that kind of thing. Working with it, you got to a point where you did feel "Oh, yeah. This wood is really nice" – Parana Pine and Douglas Fir. And sometimes the smell of the wood, it was a turn on.

With the joists holding the frames, you put the roof on next?

Dave: Yes. There was always this problem of "Why a flat roof?", because we heard so many problems about flat roofs leaking. The way Walter Segal had designed the roof, the covering of it wouldn't be fixed, it would be able to expand.

On the joists we laid wood-wool slabs. But they're not fixed; they're just laid together, butting against each other. Then you put the felt over, but it's not fixed down – it loosely fits over. At the edges, you build a little frame round it to protect the edges from the wind. To hold the felt really down, there's two tonnes of gravel.

So basically what you have is three surfaces. You've got the wood-wool slab, then you've got the felting, and then you've got the gravel. The gravel is to protect it from direct sunlight and also to hold the rain water. The wood-wool slabs can expand and contract as freely as they want to. And the felt can expand as freely as it wants to. Whereas if it was in a fixed position, it would try to expand and contract and eventually split. That's where you get leaks. None of the houses have had any leaks at all.

We had a contractor come in to put the felt down. We thought that for inexperienced people to put tar down, hot tar, it would probably be asking a bit much.

Having done the roof, we had protection. So we could store material in the lower part of the house, and if it rained, it was just nice knowing there was something over the top of your head.

Did you put the outside walls up next?

Dave: No – after the joisting was done we could put the floor in.

Barbara: But before the floor-boards, we did the plumbing, the central heating, the wiring.

Dave: Before the floor-boards went down, it was so much easier to get into the joists, and drill through the joists, and pull the wiring through, and pull all the plastic plumbing through.

Does the central heating system use plastic plumbing?

Dave: Yes; it does.

Did you find it easy to use?

Dave: It was great.

Putting down the floor-boards, I had a nail go through – it hit one of the pipes. I had to go underneath, and cut the pipe and joint it. It was easy: just cut, glue the new fitting on, and that was it. And there was no flame.

I did have to do the gas services, for the boiler and the cooker, in copper. It was tested by the gas people before they turned the gas on.

Had you ever done anything like that before?

Dave: Never. I wasn't looking forward to it. Barbara, are you asleep?

Barbara: No.

Dave: It looked like you had your eyes closed. You're supposed to be chiming in.

Barbara: I can't get a word in edgeways.

Dave: Oh, sorry.

Barbara: Keep going.

Dave: Didn't you do some of the wiring?

Barbara: Yes. Not a lot at that stage; I did more of the plumbing. I was just like the little apprentice. I'd be told to stick this pipe here and that one there, mix the solvents.

Dave: You did a lot of gluing as well.

Barbara: Yes. And I put all the insulating stuff around it.

Dave: Under the ground floor, there's rockwool between the joisting, and Mastercladding sheeting underneath – which I made in three pieces so that I could remove it and get access to the pipework.

You put also rockwool in the roof.

After we did the services, we put the floor-boards down; they were tongue-and-grooved.

Did some people use chipboard?

Dave: No; everybody used tongue-and-grooved throughout the house.

Barbara: Most people have got it covered up though.

Dave: Most people have put carpet right the way throughout.

After the flooring, we went onto putting up the walls. By that time you'd have had to exactly work out where you wanted windows.

It sounds as though you were modifying your design as you went along.

Dave: Yes; almost that. We had a rough idea what it was going to be. You did have to modify, because you'd come up against problems. Or you'd be inside the building and you'd feel that you wanted this a certain way. It started coming more closely in your head where you wanted your windows.

We hadn't really planned on putting any windows in at the back because we didn't own much land at the back. But when we were building, we negotiated to buy some extra land from the neighbour's garden. So then we wanted windows to look out onto it.

We had the option to bring in a window glazing company – people that make aluminium frames. When we looked at it, we wanted a lot of windows, and it would have been an astronomical amount of money. Plus, it would have changed the character of the whole house, to have all this metal. Considering that it was originally a wooden designed house with wooden windows, it just seemed away from the real idea. And also I felt, begrudgingly, that I'd have another company working on my house. I didn't fancy that at all. Some people did have all their window frames built by this company, and had them installed by them. I kind of compromised. I decided that wherever I wanted to have windows that opened, I would buy the aluminium ones from the company – but we installed them.

I'll put the windows in perspective. There's actually 81 windows, 81 pieces of glass, in this house. Of those 81 pieces, 19 were openers. They were the only ones the company were involved with.

Barbara: They still had to be beaded in the same way. It was the same amount of work for us.

Dave: You can imagine the amount of work that went into the frames. You do your linings, and then you've got the sealed units in place. And then each one takes eight pieces of beading.

Did you use power tools to make the frames?

Dave: I used a router. I did it inside. There were no walls, just plastic sheeting hanging down, throughout the winter. And I was inside, up to all hours, twelve, one o'clock at night.

Barbara: He slept and breathed windows.

Dave: I was living in here where the sawdust from the router would pile up. You'd walk in, and it would be like a permanent workshop – more like a production line – producing all these frames.

Barbara: Then I had them all upstairs being stained and varnished. I had to stain them twice and varnish them twice. And they were big things, all lying around.

Dave: I was getting demoralized with the windows, because all the other houses had their windows glazed.

Barbara: We felt well behind at that point. Our neighbours didn't have theirs divided up. We've got transoms. Their windows are just rectangles.

Dave: To us, it was just like sticking with the faith, being really involved in the whole production of the house. I'm not trying to say that ours is better than the others. But where Walter Segal was coming from, in the terms of the aesthetics of wood – it just felt nice to stick to that as closely as possible. I didn't really want to lose the original concept of "Here you are, an opportunity to build your own house from scratch". I didn't want to bastardize it with outside influence, a thing that wasn't even part of the plan, just in order to get into it quicker.

I felt at the time "Jesus, we really are taking too much time over this". Looking at it now, I'm glad we took that extra time. Even though it seemed like we were behind, we weren't really. The first people moved in in eighteen months; we moved in in two-and-a-half years. It wasn't that we took long; I mean, we had two kids, plus during the last phase of it, Barbara was pregnant.

How much time were you spending on the project?

Barbara: Initially, Dave was working; and we'd be up here at weekends, and he'd come up an odd day in the week. Towards the end, to make a big push, I was more or less the breadwinner, and then Dave was up here five days a week.

Dave: When I first started off, I was working up on the market.

Barbara: That's why I used to spend Saturdays up here on my own trying to get a bit done. Saturday's a busy day on the market, and he'd always be working. Sundays we'd go up together and work on the house, with each of us taking turns at keeping an eye on the children. Then Dave might spend a couple of days in the week as well up here.

How did you divide the work up between you?

Barbara: I used to have to get stuff ready for him, basically. If we were going to do walls, I'd have to have all my plasterboard ready painted. So I might come up on a Saturday and paint twenty plasterboards; and when I'd painted the twenty, I'd go back and start on the first one, with the second coat.

We had to plan when we were together. There are some jobs that you must have two people for – say, putting up the walls – even if one of us is just the dog's body who holds the bits. There would be jobs where he'd just need me there to hold things. So I'd try and get it all ready for the times when we'd be up together.

Dave: With the walls, Barbara did the battens. Her work wasn't really that easy: they had to be cut to length; then they had to be drilled; they had to be stained and varnished; then they had to be rebated at the bottom to take the skirting.

We prepared our stuff before it went up. Some people didn't paint the plasterboard first. They painted it when it was in position, but they had to be careful round all the edges not to spill over and paint the battens – so much tedious work. We found out through other people's errors.

What are the walls made of?

Dave: There's wood-wool slabs, the same as the roof. Outside the wood-wool slab is 'Glazel', a type of cladding. It's only about 4 mm thick. It acts like a skin.

Barbara: It's vitreous; it's fired.

And it's in different colours for different houses. Can you saw it?

Dave: No. You can score it, and then crack it. You've got to get the knack. It comes in a standard size, 2.3 metres in length and 600 mm wide. Where there's windows, you have to cut it to length. Each sheet cost us £20; it was expensive.

You're creating a sandwich for the wall. It's got the Glazel outside, 4 mm thick, then you've got 50 mm thick wood-wool slab, then you've got plasterboard with a Styrofoam backing for insulation. The Styrofoam is about 25 mm thick.

You're sandwiching that between two battens, which are bolted together. This holds it. You just keep putting the three pieces of the sandwich together, and put a batten and bolt it, and go round like that. It's basically then that you put the window frames in, and they give it more rigidity.

So the philosophy is that putting it all together is a simple mechanical task.

Dave: Yes. You could think of Meccano. But every single piece had to be cut. The wood-wool slab had to be cut to the right length, the plasterboard had to be cut, the Glazel, the battens. And every house was different. We all had different size windows, different style windows, different places where our windows went.

Barbara: The internal walls were two sheets of plasterboard with a wood-wool slab in the middle.

Dave: You hold them together with battens again. The way it's done, you could remove the wall and reposition it. You can take down most of the internal walls. But one internal wall is fixed. It has a St Andrew's cross in the middle, to give rigidity to the framing. There's one on the upper floor as well. They're between the two central frames.

Barbara: Before we actually started to build, our number one aim was to get a house. The building was like the obstacle – we had to build the thing. We weren't mad-keen DIY people by any means. My aim was that we'd just pay people; we'd do the minimum. My dream was to pay as many people as possible.

But that isn't the way that it worked out. As you got started, the bug got you. It almost became a point of honour to do everything ourselves.

Some people did get people in.

Dave: Even though they did get people in, they might not be satisfied.

Why?

Barbara: It wasn't done that well. It wasn't up to the selfbuilder's standards.

You realize that it's a mystique, isn't it? Like, most workmen don't do jobs that brilliantly; it's just a job. Who's going to be a perfectionist about just a job you're going to get paid for? Obviously, there's a professional skill – it's got to done to a certain level – but it's just not going to be the same.

Dave spent ages getting all his pipes straight. At the end of the day, it probably didn't matter if they weren't that straight. But if you know, even if you can't see them – it's all neatly laid out under there.

Dave: A lot of those things you do see for a while, while you're building. You see the wires hanging about. You see the pipes hanging about. And people are visiting. So I wasn't going from that standpoint, but you yourself know what the thing was like, what kind of work you've done. To me, it's your own self-esteem; it's your product. When I look at the walls, I remember Barbara because she did all the staining. People can look, and I can say "Well, I remember the problem I had with that". It's you; the building becomes you. It's hard to explain.

Explaining to the person who's not built their own house, they must think "These people must be freaks" – or DIY nuts or whatever.

How were you learning the skills? How did you learn the electrics and the plumbing? Did you learn from other people working on the project?

Dave: They give you the basic knowledge that you need. Prior to the start of the building, Walter Segal and a selfbuilder from the first scheme gave instruction on the basic plumbing, carpentry skills. And we learned through observation and some books.

So that was an advantage of working in a group then?

Dave: Yes. Somebody's already done what you're about to undertake.

Barbara: The worst thing would be to be the leaders. We were comfortably positioned, because if you're at the bottom, you're totally depressed, especialy if you're finding it difficult. A couple of people did have a bit of a struggle. In the middle, you're nicely positioned, because there's enough gone on ahead for you to go around and they tell you all the pitfalls – and they've usually worked out a few little tricks to make life easier.

A couple of our friends invented this 'third man'. Some jobs were the pits, like getting those ceiling plasterboards up, especially the long ones. With two of you, they bend in the middle. The 'third man' was a big piece of wood on a wobbly stick. Like a lady putting up her washing on the washing line with the old-fashioned fork – it was something like that. You prop it up, then one of you has free hands to pull the board across.

Battens would support the plasterboard then?

Dave: Well, the battens are there, but there's a one-by-one strip above the plasterboard. The plasterboard's nailed to that. And then it's sandwiched by the battens underneath. The battens are called a 'sacrificial lining'. In a fire, they're protecting the other wood. And they stop the plasterboard from suddenly coming down and letting the flames upstairs. [That is, the battens are fixed to the exposed lower part of the joists, so protecting them in fire and also helping to hold up the plasterboard.]

What did you find was the most difficult part of the job?

Dave: The manhole – I was really peeved about that.

We had contractors do the road. And under the road, there's a huge cavern which takes all the waste from the houses. All the drainage leads into this cavern. And then it's pumped up the hill to the top of the road.

When they put the cavern in, they put manholes strategically placed so that we could feed into it. But we all had to dig trenches so that we could meet up with it, and then dig our own manhole. And that was one of the hardest parts of the job. I would have liked to have used a small JCB. I started digging to find out where the services were, so I wouldn't have to worry about the JCB tearing up a gas line or a water line or the electric. I started digging and kept on going. I ended up digging my six-foot deep manhole, and then the trench that links it with the manhole to the cavern. So I did the whole thing by spade and boot. That must have been three or four weeks of digging.

I didn't mind. Having done it, I thought "Shit, I've got it done".

What happens to the rainwater from the flat roof?

Dave: Most of the rain water stays on the roof until it evaporates. Only the excess runs of into a drain to the cavern.

What sort of other people built their houses here? Were some of them skilled trades-people?

Dave: There's skilled trades-people here. One is a chippy, two are plasterers. But their skills as plasterers weren't needed. And not many of the carpenter's skills were necessary. When you look at the joints that were required, most people are capable of doing those.

All of us, in the first instance, had had nothing to do with house building as such.

Did everybody succeed, or did some people give up?

Dave: No-one gave up. They might have taken a longer time. But everyone had finished within three years of the start.

And most people were in paid jobs outside at the same time?

Dave: Yes; it was evening-time, and weekends.

During the later stages, I took time off from the business. I wanted to finish the house; it was taking up too much of our time. So it was imperative to actually finish it.

We moved in before we were officially to move in. It meant that we would get more done, being here. I worked till three, four o'clock in the morning sometimes. I'd put a mattress on the floor and sleep amongst the sawdust. It was great.

When I got up, I could actually go into the kitchen and put the kettle on and get some simple food together. One of the first things we did, before we had beds, or carpet down, was to put the kitchen in. That was really nice: no more sandwiches! Now it was hot soups.

Have you got any general advice that you'd give to someone who was thinking of building their own home?

Dave: It's easy to say "I'd love everybody to be involved in building their own place". But not everybody can do what we did.

Why not?

Dave: The practical and technical side of building the house is within the ability of any reasonably healthy person. But the actual logistics involved in re-arranging your life around the building process takes more getting into.

But to the ordinary person, I think it's an opportunity to be involved in creating your own environment. It might not mean that you do everything yourself. This house has shown me that everybody's capable of doing it on the practical side. That's the first message. You don't have to be anything special. You develop into something special once you've started – I think so, anyhow. We're just Barbara and Dave. We were given an opportunity to do something. At first, we didn't quite comprehend what we were getting into, but having gotten into it, it was for our own benefit.

Barbara: There were many times that I swore that, if I'd known how hard it was going to be, I'd never have started. Once you were doing it, you didn't have any choice. There were lots of times it was like a prison sentence; you just have to march onwards. I can remember thinking many times "If I'd bloody known it was going to be like this. . .".

Would you advice somebody else to do it?

Barbara: Well, the thing is, I would now because I've got my nice house. It's lovely here. I wouldn't want to live anywhere else. And I can now look back and say "It's all worthwhile". But I can remember in the middle . . .

Dave: We were cussing each other out; we had arguments and fights. The kids were getting the wrong end of our personality. But there were times when it was really nice, because people would come to visit us while we were working on the house, and it was like we got a recharge for our batteries. They'd come and give some encouragement; they'd come and bring some food. Little things like that could happen normally when you weren't on a project and you wouldn't think anything of it. But when it happened, it was great because it was almost like: Yeah, we knew what we were doing it for.

For a lot of people, it helps you. It becomes a discipline. You have to maintain a routine even when repetition is all that you're allowed to do. You have to stick to it even when you don't want to.

It helps to build your body and spirit. And at the end of the day, your labour becomes of more worth. Rather than working for somebody, you're now working for yourself.

Barbara: It's more than just doing it to save some money. It is a definite point of growth; it's a definite development for you. Whatever else happens in your life, you can say "I built the house". It does give you a lot more confidence.

Dave: It's back to that thing, that you're involved – even if you don't build your own house but are liaising with someone who is putting together the house that you're going to live in. Besides, it's a big commitment to actually buy a house. It would be so much nicer to know that you were paying off for something that you had a hand in actually putting together – and at a fraction of the cost, in our particular case.

To build a house is a lot cheaper than buying an existing house.

Any idea what this one would be valued at now?

Dave: One of our neighbours had an estate agent come up and look at theirs, and they valued it a year ago at £75,000, something like that. The house wasn't finished. The garden wasn't landscaped, or anything like that.

The house has stood up well, hasn't it?

Dave: It's been through the hurricane. We had the hurricane the year before last [in 1987]. No damage happened to any of the houses up here; no damage at all. Nothing moved.

Barbara: There was a bit of a sway. It was like being on a boat! I could feel it moving.

Dave: I feel that this house is a really sturdy house.

It's a simple design. And the old guy knew what he was about. And I still can't say enough praises about the guy. What he's done, from a simple Swiss chalet, was to develop it into a house. They've got these houses in Australia, Canada, the US, Jamaica. That says a lot. It's like it's spawned a generation of house builders, without sending us through any formal training, apart from practical training on site. Which is great.

Did you build the stairs here as well? The normal stair design is pretty complicated.

Dave: Yes; but that was his design again. Simplicity!

Barbara: That was pretty complicated: cutting up all those treads. They had to fit exactly.

Dave: I built templates. I made sure the templates were right before I committed it to the actual hardwood. I had to make sure that all those kites were right. But it was worth it.

The stairs look distinctive.

Dave: It's a dream house. I think it's our dream house. Some people think of a dream house as a great, big mansion, but I think now that a dream house is something that you had a hand in building. That's the real dream house.

7

A GROUP OF TRADESMEN
The Underwood Self-Build Housing Association

THIS SELFBUILD GROUP was one of the most professional that you could expect to find. Of the dozen members, all but two were in trades directly related to house building. As a result, they built their houses remarkably quickly, in a little over a year. This was achieved in their spare time, although they did use some subcontract labour as well.

The group was set up by Wadsworth and Heath Ltd, who specialized in setting up and managing selfbuild groups. They found the land (in Nottinghamshire), arranged the finance for the project, collected the people together, supplied the plans, obtained Planning Permission and Building Regulations approval, kept the accounts, reclaimed VAT, ordered some materials, and gave general advice.

When the group was originally set up, the time planned for the project was eighteen months, but the people in the group decided to go for twelve months instead. In the end, they took a month more than this, but even so, that is remarkably fast.

I had the following conversation with three of the members of the scheme: Alan Hollingworth (bricklayer), Bob Turton (carpenter and joiner) and Steve Bourne (ex-bricklayer). Later, Alan's wife, Sandra, joined us.

☆   ☆   ☆   ☆   ☆

Can I ask you first how you came to hear about this scheme?

Alan: Wadsworth and Heath were advertising in the local paper, about four years ago [1985].

Bob: They were getting a group together of people who knew they wanted to selfbuild. They wanted twelve members altogether. The Council were selling the plots off: there were 40 plots for selfbuild.

Steve: Wadsworth and Heath obviously look out for that.

Alan: And the Council wanted a selfbuild group. Wadsworth and Heath got in touch with the Council, and Wadsworth's bought this land – or put a deposit down on it.

They advertised. And they vetted you to make sure you could afford it when you'd finished.

Bob: How I got to know about it was that Alan was working on the site where I worked and he was asking "Are you interested in building your own house?".

I said if it was possible I'd like to build my own house, but I said it was an impossibility with the money required and everything else involved. He said "Well, I think you'll find out, if you look through this scheme, it won't cost you much to start off. You don't have to sell your own house straightaway".

So I looked through the scheme. We were interested. Then I went to one of the meetings. I was more or less the last member.

Did a lot of people want to come on the scheme? Did Wadsworth's reject people?

Steve: I think at the first meeting they wanted everybody.

Alan: When I joined there was about four members. There was about half the numbers required when the scheme got going.

Bob: There's five bungalows with three bedrooms; there's four three-beds; and then there's three four-beds. That makes twelve in all.

That's a little bit unusual for a scheme like this, isn't it? Quite often, they're virtually all the same to make it fair.

Bob: I think that with this scheme that's why it took off fairly well.

The majority of us were house-owners already. So we didn't want to come into a scheme where the houses all looked the same. We've all got individual houses. I think that was the beauty of it.

Could you influence the design of these houses?

Alan: No; not the exterior. We've altered the insides to a degree. We just moved doorways and the odd wall; that's all. Steve's got the only original bungalow.

Bob: You can do anything you want inside, but you couldn't alter the structures. I wanted to alter the roof, but they said, No; I couldn't, because if they'd allowed one person to, it would have snowballed all the way through. They said "We'd rather you alter it after the scheme" – which was a pain.

Alan: I think the Council made the group have different designs. The Council knew that every house in this area was going to be a different design because all the people were doing them themselves.

Steve: Didn't the Council make us have so many bungalows?

Alan: Yes; four. But then somebody else joined and he wanted a bungalow, so it all got altered again.

Steve: There were so many changes that took place.

Alan: It took nearly a year before we started on site.

Bob: I think that basically we had a bit of trouble with the Council.

Steve: The choice of bricks was a tremendous problem with them.

Bob: The Council was holding us up with little niggly things. Like, they didn't like the choice of bricks we picked. We went to the brickyard with the actual Council bloke, and we said "We like these, and we like these, and we like these".

"Oh, no. You're not having any of them. They've all got to be brown."

Steve: At first, we wanted them red, and they wanted them all buff coloured. But in the end, they came back and said "You can have red ones".

Alan: – But everybody had to have them.

Bob: I think, looking back on the scheme, it was well organized. It was well organized by Wadsworth and Heath – that's their business. But we were well organized as well.

We liked it straight down the middle. You'd got to sign in and sign out. You'd got to get your hours in.

Who organized that?

Alan: There was a committee with a chairman, a foreman, a secretary, a treasurer – all from our group.

How much did Wadsworth and Heath participate in your organization?

Alan: A lot of the time they didn't participate enough, we thought. There were odd times when we could have done with their backup, but they weren't there.

Were they dealing with the Council?

Alan: Yes.

Wadsworth's had a chap come down. The Clerk of Works would come down every week or every fortnight, this old fellow, and he'd report back to the architect. The architect would come down every two months – something like that.

Wadsworth's would tell us where we were going wrong.

I think they'd got it organized to get the discounts that they do get. I mean, the roof tiles came from Scotland; they don't deliver this far down South [Mansfield]. Because Wadsworth's were doing a lot in South Shields, the firm agreed to come down here.

So from the point of view of organizing materials and getting the discount, Wadsworth's are A1. They are absolutely superb – superb discounts.

And the materials arrived when you wanted them?

Alan: Oh, we had no bother with materials.

How was the ordering done?

Bob: The chairman did the ordering.

Did you do that through Wadsworth's?

Bob: No; we could order straight from the builders' merchants.

Steve: The chairman was a quantity surveyor.

Bob: We were very lucky with tradesmen, to take a group of twelve out from the world about, and come up with most of the tradesmen that we needed.

We had two chippies, three bricklayers, a plasterer, a quantity surveyor, an electrician, a plumber.

Alan: We had one who worked in the hosiery trade, and a school teacher.

So you had two odd ones out?

Alan: Not really, because once they got into it – the school teacher, he could do a bit of plumbing.

The surveyor hadn't done much at all, but once he got into it, he did all the drainage. And he did all the paths, all the slabbing and stuff, and he was away.

And we had a cabinet maker.

Bob: We did say, at the start of the scheme, that from the scheme somebody could learn a bit of a trade out of it. You wouldn't just be an onlooker. You'd learn something. I think we all did.

Did you cross over trades yourselves then?

Alan: Oh, yes.

Bob: We tried to. But I was finding it hard because I was the only chippy. I was full-time. I couldn't do anything more because I was fully booked up.

I think that, where you've got the joinery and the bricklaying, that's full-time. That's got to carry on. OK, we did a bit of plasterboarding one night, or something like that, but we couldn't try too much because we had to keep it going. We did decide, right at the beginning, that it would only take us twelve months. It was on a schedule.

Alan: In fact, it took us thirteen months in the end.

Bob: Sometimes, I used to think that Mick [the chairman and organizer] was being a bit unfair to us. He said "We've got to push it" when it was getting a bit tight.

Alan: We did have subcontractors. We had contract plasterers, and the tiler, bricklayers, and two subcontract joiners.

Bob: We did want to put it all down ourselves, but it comes to a stage like with the roof tilers. We thought "Well, if half of us try to learn it, it would take far longer". These roof tilers came on and whopped a roof on one weekend, and we thought "We can't compete with those guys". They gave us a reasonable price. We just put the trusses on and left them to it. We were ever so pleased with them. We couldn't spare our time for it.

Alan: Then we had a couple of lads who did double glazing. They came and put all the glass in. We had it delivered and it was all there. They just came and that was it. We had no messing about at all. Then we had some more joiners. We had another plumber at weekends. We had some more plasterers, because the one that we'd got, although he was a plasterer, he wasn't a very fast plasterer. So we had to bring some other plasterers in to give it a push.

How was the scheme financed?

Alan: By a loan from the Halifax.

Though what we found was that the surveyor who came round from the Halifax, he was undervaluing what we'd spent. So that, each month, we weren't getting enough money off the Halifax to pay the bills. So we were losing discount. We kept telling him this. At times we were very, very tight. We couldn't go to certain merchants.

We proved it in the end, because he owed us £40,000 on one house. So we were right, but he just wouldn't have it.

[The surveyor was undervaluing work in progress and only giving full value to finished houses. But the Halifax's advances were tied to the 'value' of the site as it progressed, and so were too little.]

Bob: His policy is to do that, but it was a bit of a drawback for us.

Did the Halifax give you a group mortgage on the whole lot?

Alan: We borrowed the money off them to build the houses. Everybody's got their mortgages now with the Halifax, bar me.

At the end of the scheme, you had to sort your mortgage out yourself.

Bob: At the end, the Halifax more or less owned the place. They came and opened the first house. They'd got the key, and the Halifax sign—

Steve: —and their photograph in the local paper.

Bob: We were all quite surprised at the local interest around. While we were building, people were stopping in their cars and saying "We want to know where we can buy one of these". And we had to say "I'm sorry, it's all private build".

Alan: What happened was:

The Council sold these plots off – they were advertised in the paper. Some people queued overnight for these plots. It was first come first served, and they were very cheap.

How much were these plots being sold for?

Alan: Eight, nine, ten thousand. £17,500 was the most expensive.

Steve: We got like a bulk lot. Because we bought twelve, we got them cheaper.

Alan: It was about £6,500 per plot, on average.

Bob: They've just sold the last plot off at the top. That's gone for £25,000, but that's four years on.

Have you any idea how much Wadsworth's made out of the deal?

Steve: About £2,000 each house: £24,000 altogether.

Were you happy with that?

Alan: Yes; because they sorted all the VAT out. They go through the books and tell you what to claim.

Steve: To organize all that for £2,000 each is well worth it, I reckon.

Alan: They were working for over a year. We took nearly a year to set up, and a year to build. It's not a lot of money really.

Bob: Sometimes we weren't too satisfied, sometimes we thought the information wasn't coming through.

Steve: But we had a very good man from them.

Bob: In general, we made sure we had regular meetings, every fortnight. We kept our noses to the grindstone because we had to put the hours in.

How did you organize that?

Alan: We worked 25 hours a week minimum. Well, it started as 20 and ended up as 30. If you put more hours in, that was to the good of the scheme. But the odd person only put in the bare minimum, or less. If they put less in, they had to make that up the following week and pay the fine of £5 an hour for every hour that they were short.

Bob: Many a man got some fines.

Are you saying that they had to do an hour extra and be fined £5?

Alan: Yes.

Steve: They did to start with, but then there was so much uproar about it that the committee cut it out.

Alan: And they just paid the fine.

Steve: One chap went wild about it. He said "I'm either paying the fine or doing the hours, but not both". So we did drop it halfway, and it was a straight fine.

Bob: We did try to keep it as strict as we could, because if you let one get away with it, the others will want it. Eventually we had to tell this chap that he was into a one-twelfth share as much as anybody else. He was going to benefit as much as I was.

Bob: He could never keep to the time; he just rolled up when he wanted.

Alan: And then he'd be working late at night, and nobody would be here, so you wouldn't know whether he was working or not.

Bob: We depended on honesty. You had to put your hours down yourself. You had to sign in when you came in, and sign out when you left, and at the end of the week you had to tot your hours up.

What happened if you were sick? You didn't have to make that time up, did you?

Bob: If you were sick, you had to phone another member and then bring a sick note. But I don't think anybody was sick.

Alan: I was ill with a bad eye. I couldn't see anything, so I had a few days off.

The electrician went to Barbados to bury a relative, and he was gone a week. *Laughter.* So he paid his fine.

Steve: All these rules were written down somewhere.

But looking back on it, anybody who did pay fines was on a winner. They were better off letting other people build it for them and just paying fines. You could have got a house built by doing that.

Alan: Steve worked a lot of hours up here because he was on shifts at the factory. Yet other people were only putting in a few. So really it wasn't fair on Steve.

Was there a lot of aggro about this?

Bob: There wasn't a lot of aggro; but we thrashed it out at the meetings. That was part of the meetings. If there's any disagreements, you've got to thrash it out. We hadn't got to hide away and think "Oh, I shan't say anything". You've got to put it to them. I think they were good, the meetings. They told you how the money was running, how the site was running, what were we short of, the timekeeping. They were a good thing.

At the time, we all thought it was a drudgery because it was extra hours.

Bob Turton's house

When did you have the meetings?

Bob: They were usually on a Monday night.

And most weekends you were up here on the site?

Steve: Oh, without fail, Saturdays and Sundays.

Alan: And three nights a week, and a week of your holidays. So everybody had the same week off to work up here.

How did it feel that some of you were getting big houses built, and some of you were only getting bungalows, but you were all putting in roughly the same hours?

Bob: It all depends on the person who's taking the mortgage. It all depends on what you want to afford.

Alan: You see, Bob's got two lads. So therefore Bob wanted a four-bedroomed house. Basically, there's not much difference in the floor areas.

Bob: The only difference is in the actual style.

Alan: The price only varies with the size of the plot.

Bob: The prices that were quoted to us at the start of the scheme were a year behind. It was a bit of a blow at the end of the scheme, when all of a sudden they said the prices on some of them were going up. My God!
    We'd put all the work in, and then they go and hit us with that.

Alan: We went to the meeting, and the bungalows went up £5,000, from £23,000.

Bob: We knew there was an increase, but not that much. The scheme had more or less ended and they came out with these figures then.

Steve: It was a bit of a disaster.

Alan: It was a disaster because the three-bedroomed houses were dirt cheap.

Steve: I'll tell you what happened because I wanted one of those three-bedroomed houses:
    Wadsworth's laid out all the prices, three-bedroomed bungalows, three-bedroomed houses, four-bedroomed houses. Now the cheapest on the site were going to be the three-bedroomed bungalows. I couldn't understand why three-bedroomed bungalows were cheaper than three-bedroomed houses. So I thought "I won't have a house, I'll have a bungalow because they're cheaper". And all through the scheme, we were led to believe that the bungalows were going to be cheaper. But right at the end of the scheme, they changed it round.

Alan: Right at the end of the scheme, when you'd only got a week or so to get a mortgage sorted out, they bumped the bungalows up £5,000.

Steve: We paid for an independent valuer, a month into the scheme, to look at the drawings and get some sort of price guide. And we all agreed at a meeting that, at the end of the scheme, we'd get him in again to give us a true valuation.
    Right through the scheme, we were going on the impression that our bungalows were going to be cheaper than anything else on the site.

Then the valuer came and said "Now I've seen them in the flesh", sort of thing, "I've changed my mind, and the bungalows are nicer than I thought they were going to be".

Bob: He altered his mind from the drawing to the actual thing.

So the price was done on the valuation, rather than the cost of the materials that had gone into the house?

Alan: Yes – and with the size of the plot. [So the houses were not costed individually. Instead, the total cost of the whole scheme was divided according to the final valuations of the individual houses. This fixed the prices to be paid for different houses.]

Wadsworth's give you a price when you go to the first meeting. And they estimated the price of my bungalow at £23,450. It ended up at £27,800.

And that was about two years later?

Alan: That's right. There was about a year of meetings before we even started. Then the thirteen months building. So two years later they'd gone up nearly £5,000.

Bob: Looking at it now, it was fair; but at the time we didn't think so.

Steve: That was the biggest argument we ever had, over these prices.

Bob: It caused a lot of bitterness, that.

Against Wadsworth and Heath?

Steve: No; it was against the valuer, who we'd paid money to, to get it wrong. We'd paid money to get a professional valuer in, and he got it totally wrong.

Alan: And against the other members because they didn't want, obviously, their houses to go up. Now the bungalows were built first, and we'd been in here. I'd been in five months, paying £160 a month rent to the Association. We'd paid all that money in and got it all nicely furnished. So therefore we'd got to pay the extra five. You either paid the five thousand, or you were out on the street.

Steve: It was in the minutes that we agreed to go by the final valuation. We had no say in it. We'd agreed that.

Who appointed this valuer? Was it Wadsworth's or you?

Bob: We did. We had a separate valuer for ourselves.

Steve: He was a totally independent valuer. We got the valuer in. He came in, and just by the drawings, gave us guide lines on the prices.

So we went right through the scheme on the assumption that the bungalows were going to be the cheapest, and then the valuer came in again and said "Oh, no; I like the bungalows better now".

We couldn't do anything because there were five of us [with bungalows] against seven [with houses]. All the other seven were going to save money, and we were going to lose money. So the vote was bound to go their way.

That was the biggest argument.

Bob: It sort of broke the scheme up. Well, it didn't break the scheme up—

Steve: —the scheme was over.

Bob: We'd all been working for the same, and all to be split like that!

Steve: But we've got to give them due: that we asked them to even the situation up a bit, and they did do.

Alan: We asked them for another £1,000 each.

Steve: They paid another £500 for their houses.

Alan: We paid another £5,000.

Bob: It was about the worst blow.

Steve: At the time, it was a severe blow.

Alan: – Because one or two of us were struggling to get a mortgage.

Steve: Can you remember, we came out here and we didn't do a thing that afternoon?

Alan: No; we didn't do a stroke.

Then one of the couples – well, they'd left within a few months.

They sold up?

Alan: They had to because they were struggling with the mortgage repayments.

That brings us onto the question: how much were they actually worth?

Steve: At the time, about £40,000.

Alan: £40,000 to £45,000, something like that.

Bob: The price the couple sold at had got a big jump on it, which I suppose was being greedy in our eyes.

Steve: But you've got to blame Wadsworth and Heath because everybody knows that a three-bedroomed bungalow is worth more than a three-bedroomed house. If we all know that, a valuer should know that, and Wadsworth and Heath should know that.

Bob: Time has healed it. Time has healed. As time has gone by, prices have gone up.

Steve: Yes; it seems nothing now.

Alan: They work out at £80,000 now.

So you're laughing all the way to bank.

Alan: Something like that.
  Ah, but we don't want to sell. Though Barry left next door; he's doing another selfbuild.

He's in another group scheme?

Bob: He's doing a single selfbuild. He's doing it all himself; he's getting his own men in.

Alan: Then there's three others left.

Do you know why they left?

Bob: The obvious reason is money – take the money and run.

Alan: One of them couldn't afford it, for starters. And the other one – he's done something out of it.
  And these two are for sale next door.

Does that mean that, after a couple of years, half of you have left?

Bob: Yes.

The other people I've spoken to who've built it themselves, they'd become attached to their houses. It doesn't sound as though you were?

Steve: I think it's money mainly.

Alan: It's a case of taking the profit, isn't it? Round here, there's a bug. And they've all bought more of these plots. And they're all going to move again, all these people round here moving.

They've done it once, and they're all going to do it again then?

Alan: There's one chap round the corner, and he's done one every year for the last five years. He's on his sixth.

Bob: Selfbuild in general is a good scheme.

Alan: I wish I'd have done it twenty years ago.

Bob: I'd recommend it to a young person. If they get stuck into it for a year, it's a good discipline for a year.

In your group, you had a lot of skilled trades-people, didn't you?

Bob: I've heard of some groups who might be lucky to get one or two tradesmen out of the twelve.

Alan: We'd got a good mixture.

There was a sum in the bill for subcontractors. I think we went over that, but then again, we saved on the interest on the money that we borrowed from the Halifax. And we did get some good subbies to do some of the work. Without them, we wouldn't have got it done in twelve months. It's a case of you either go for eighteen months and do it all yourselves, or you get subbies in. We had some subcontract bricklayers in to do the four three-bedroomed houses.

Even though you had three bricklayers in the group?

Alan: There's a lot of bricks in these!

We were doing the footings on these bungalows. There's 6,000 bricks in them. Three of us would do one of these footings on a Saturday and a Sunday, finished. We'd turn one out a weekend.

So we did all the footings to get them in, because this ground is like a sponge. We decided that we'd do the four-bedroomed houses at weekends, and let the others out.

What time of year did you start?

Alan: We started in March, but then we stopped for a few weeks because of the Council.

Bob: We finished at the end of March the following year.

Steve: Three bricklayers would never have built this lot.

Alan: Not unless they worked full-time.

Bob: One or two joiners wouldn't have done this. You've got to really get shifting.

Alan: You've got to get one finished and get someone in it, so you can rent it to that member whose house it's going to be.

Bob: Per plot, I think it was an average of around £2,000 for subcontracting.

How did you decide which buildings you were going to finish first, so people could move in?

Alan: We discussed it in a meeting.

Bob: It depended on who wanted one first.

You didn't draw lots?

Alan: No, no, no.

We made a plan of attack. It didn't always work though.

It sounds as though it all went fairly smoothly, but did you have any big upsets or big difficulties?

Alan: No; not really.

Bob: I think we thrashed them out at the meetings.

Alan: As for problems on site, we had a very good building inspector. I don't very often praise these people, but he was quite good and he was helpful.

I don't think we had any problems apart from the mud.

Bob: The majority of us were tradesmen, and we knew how to get on with it.

Alan: I think the biggest problem was that the non-tradesmen didn't like the tradesmen telling them what to do.

Bob: Mick, the organizer, used to tell us "You can't let other non-tradesmen just stand around and watch". You have to buck them up a bit. You have to say to them "Look, you're not here to smoke. You've got to pull your weight as much as anybody".

Alan: They didn't really realize that it's alright bitting-and-bobbing at home, but they didn't really realize what a building site was going to be like. And I think it hit them, especially when we were doing the footings. We about killed the plumber.

What was he doing? Mixing for you?

Alan: No; carrying bricks – about three at a time.

Bob: Now the teacher, he found it was a strain, but he'd done it before while he was a student. He used to go on building sites, so it wasn't a first thing.

In general, I think we'd got a good age – one really old man and one really young man. And it gave us a good average age, and good average all-round tradesmen.

Not too many problems arose because there was a way out of it. A tradesman could work his way out of it. I think you'd come across a lot of problems, if there weren't many tradesmen about, because you'd just be stuck then.

A tradesman would be going round telling other people how to get on, so he wouldn't get his own job done. I think I found that myself. Quite honestly, I'm quite good at my job, but perhaps I'm not the fastest bloke. So the organizer, Mick, he used to really get onto my back. He'd say "Look, I want you to stay here, no matter what happens anywhere else. If somebody comes up 'Oh, Bob, I can't get this skirting to go back', I don't want you leaving your job". And he said "Let them get on with it, what they can. You carry on with what you've got. Once you stop, the whole lot stops".

So you had an organizer and a foreman. What was the difference between them?

Bob: Mick was a quantity surveyor. He organized the materials, and he was the chairman of the meetings, and things like that. He used to slander us at the meetings. He put a lot of pressure on me.

Often-times you'd think "Oh, I don't know why he's getting on at me". And then, when you had five minutes to yourself, you could analyse it and think "He's right".

One of his sayings was "You've got to take the bouquets when they come, but when the mud starts flying, you've got to stand there and take that as well".

Steve: We all took notice of him because basically he knew a lot.

Bob: He would say "If I've got stuff coming on site, you can't all stand there gawping at it. You've got to get stuck into it".

Steve: He knew what he was talking about. He could see through every trade, if you know what I mean.

Bob: He did all the ordering for most trades, so he could see what was coming.

There's a difference between this group and the other people that I've seen, and that is in where the women fit in. I guess that the women didn't fit in here at all?

Alan: Well . . .

What happened was that all the frames for the houses were delivered to one house. And the woman would stain them. All my skirting and architrave, I took it to my house, and my wife stained it. Only some people did that. Others didn't, and they complained that theirs wasn't stained enough!

Some wives didn't attempt, and some wives did.

We had a couple of get-togethers; we had a big bonfire-night party.

Bob: But I think that some of the women felt that they were pushed out.

Alan: Yes. They didn't have any say at any meeting. Which was wrong really.

Bob: I do think that it was a fault that we didn't organize the women in.

Alan: It was a fault on Wadsworth's part.

Steve: You want to keep it as simple as possible at these meetings. With the women, it could drag onto half-one in the morning, couldn't it?

Bob: The majority of the women felt they'd got their nose twisted a bit. At the end of the day, it's as much my wife's house as mine. She had to look after the kids at weekends while I was working.

I must give credit to Barry Heald [from Wadsworth and Heath]. At the beginning, he used to say to us "It won't be all compliments. Some days, you'll feel like chucking it all up. You'll think 'Sod this. Why should I work every weekend?'". And it's too true – it's a strain on you.

Alan: You get fed up, because all day long you're laying bricks.

You're doing that for your work as well.

Alan: That's true. And then you've got to come here and do it again. Steve was alright because he works at a factory. Steve used to be a bricklayer.

Steve: I was alright, but you wouldn't want to do it like that for seven days a week.

Alan: By the time Sunday night would come and we'd done a footing, we were done! Then the next day, I'd got to go to work and I'd got to start laying again. It was hard work.

Steve: When you've finished Friday, you've had enough, haven't you?

Bob: I didn't find it too much because my trade can vary.

So at times you were really fed up with it?

Alan: Yes. Sometimes you just didn't feel like doing it.

Bob: I think it was true that about six months into the scheme we were all really tired. And you could tell with the members as well. You'd have a little bit of an argument, perhaps a comment to someone, and SNAP! You'd think "Hold on a minute. Don't fly off the handle". But as I say, time heals, time does heal.

If you'd have come up here when we'd just had that letter [in which the cost of the bungalows went up £5,000], there'd have been a constant BLEEP on your tape. *Laughter.*

It was hard going. It was hard going, but as I said, I would advise it for people. The thing that I liked about it was that it was only twelve or thirteen months.

Alan: If you did any more, it would be too much.

Had you decided, when you started out, that you wanted to do it in only a year?

Bob: Yes. Wadsworth's had originally said eighteen months, but we said "No, we'll have it done in twelve".

Alan: I once read about this selfbuild years ago, just after I'd got married. But I thought "There's a catch in it. I fancy it, but there's a catch". Somebody was organizing one near Nottingham. I wish I'd have done it, because now I'm over forty – *laughter* – I don't want to do it again.

If I was twenty-five, I'd do a couple more. The third one, you wouldn't have a mortgage on it.

Steve: I think the catch is that there's no guarantee of success. We were working all those hours, and at times everything was just speculative.

But in the end, you must have had some houses.

Steve: But you've no idea how much they're going to cost.

Bob: But you knew, when you were building it, that you were going to have a house or bungalow for £30,000, didn't you? You were happy with that.

Steve: But no scheme can be guaranteed, or everybody would be doing it.

Did you say that you had to put some money in, when you joined the scheme?

Alan: When you first started, you paid £250 – well, £251 actually: £1 for your share to join the housing association, and £250 you put into loanstock so there was some money in the bank.

Has the Association been folded up now?

Alan: Yes; and everybody's got their money back. [£250]

Bob: It was good in the way that we had buying power because there was twelve of us.

Alan: The power was incredible. We had some brilliant discounts. We had the cheapest bricks round here.

Bob: We saved on the land; that was a bonus straightaway.

What Wadsworth's saved you on the land paid for their fees, didn't it?

Alan: Yes.
   We had all the timber from Magnet's, all the ready-mixed concrete from one place.

Bob: Yes. You've got to buy in bulk.

Alan: We weren't dealing with a lot of firms.
   All the windows and doors came from Carr's; the glass came from Carr's.

Are they sealed units?

Bob: They said "With you buying all the doors and frames, we can give you a good price on the sealed units".

Alan: It cost us another £30 or so, to have it all double glazed instead of single.

Bob: We couldn't believe it. We thought "You've got it wrong, this is single glazing". It came as a good bonus to us.

Did you have a phone on site?

Alan: Yes; in the portakabin – very useful.

We even had a flush loo. We built a block loo, breeze blocks with a tin roof on it.

Compared to some of the sites I've been on, it was a good clean site. We had very little waste.

Bob: A lot of members did take a lot of pride in the work. They wanted the best things for it.

You've got cavity wall insulation?

Steve: No; we've got 5″ Celcon Turbo blocks. They're warm, but you plug in and you can't get a fixing.

Alan: You have to get special fixings. We kept the fibreglass out; I don't believe in it.

You like to keep a cavity there?

Alan: That's what they tell you at college. It's the best thing.

Bob: We've got airbricks every six bricks along.

Are they suspended floors?

Alan: Yes.

They were going to have 2″ breeze walls. But we said "No. You can never hold them up". Then they were on about studding. I said "No; we'll have 4″ breeze walls". Which cost a little bit more.

Bob: We had all the reps down here. We kept right on the toes of the reps.

They gave us good value on the boilers, but they didn't send too many reps down to explain it to us – because we've got the new Combi boilers.

Alan: My fuel bills for here are comparable with what they were in my other house. But this is a lot warmer.

Steve: Oh, there's no problem with the central heating. It's the hot water.

Bob: It's a bit slow. But I'm prepared to wait. I'm prepared to wait for the bill to come in the door.

Alan: In these bungalows, the boiler should have been in the bathroom. We were going to put them in the kitchen to start with, but I said "No; these are going to look ugly" – because it's a massive boiler. So we put them in the utility. The water takes a long time to get to the kitchen sink.

Steve: It's a disaster.

Alan: But other than that, once it's running hot, it's that hot it's incredible.

Steve: It's alright when the central heating's on; the hot water comes through pretty instant. But in summer, when you've got it on water only, it takes an age to come through. Mine does, anyway.

What about lights, wall lights and so on?

Alan: The electrician drew up a plan, and he said 'You will have so many plugs in here, and if you want any more, it's extra'. The wall lights were extra.

Steve: You walked round with him and said what you wanted.

Alan: You paid £5 for a plug, or something like that. You only paid for materials, not for labour.

Alan Hollingworth's bungalow

Who did the decorating?

Alan: We did ourselves. When your house was ready, you painted it yourself.

What about scaffolding?

Alan: We bought all that.

We bought some off another selfbuild scheme up North. Wadsworth's put us in touch. And then we bought a load of new stuff, and when we'd finished, we sold it all off to another selfbuild group.

And we bought a dumper and two mixers. The dumper was a bad buy because the clutch went. It cost us about £500 to repair it.

Everything that we bought, we sold afterwards. We bought a portakabin – we sold that to another selfbuild group.

Bob: If we'd kept hiring scaffolding, we'd have paid through the nose.

Alan: We did hire some of our scaffolding out to other selfbuilders round here. We made a bit there.

Have you got any advice to people thinking of going into a scheme like this?

Alan: I wouldn't go on one that was any longer than twelve months. No way.

And the younger they can start to do it, the better.

Bob: But the younger they are, the less experience they've got.

Alan: But it sets you up, and the younger you can do it the better.

Bob: The thing is, you've got to get into it, be devoted to it. You've got to put that time aside for the scheme and not do anything else. If you can't put yourself a year aside and get yourself a property, it's a poor thing – if you can't help yourself along the way. You've got to be prepared to put that twelve months aside.

Alan: What you're really talking about is working a week of normal work, and half a week or more at weekends and nights. Which makes 80 hours a week.

Bob: If you're prepared to put the effort in, you'll get your reward at the end.

Alan: And you get something that you want.

Bob: You often think that it's a dark tunnel. When you start off you can't see any light at the end, and you think "My God!". *Laughter.* When you're halfway through the scheme, you can't go back, you've only got to go forward. That light at the end of the tunnel seems a long way off. You think "I've got another six months to go at this".

But looking back on it, as I say, time does heal.

Steve: There's no backing out, once you've gone six months. You're committed, or else you're going to pack up and get nothing, not a penny – all that work for nothing.

Did you make some provision in your rules for people leaving?

Steve: No; no provision.

Alan: There were two or three lads that started and then packed up, but they didn't do much.

Did they get their £250 back?

Bob: Yes.

That left openings. Which left it rather bitter, because the new people came in when the others had been working for a couple of months.

Alan: That's when the arguments started.

Bob: We thought "Well, he's just coming straight into the scheme, he's getting the one-twelfth share-out, but he's not putting all the work into it".

Alan: They should have paid more for their house. That's how it should have been, but it didn't work like that.

Bob: There was a bit of bitterness about that.

Steve: What they said at the meeting was that those hours had been done by other people.
   The real losers were those who'd worked for two months, for nothing.

Alan, as his wife, Sandra, comes in from the kitchen: Do you want a woman's point of view on all this – stuck at home, looking after kids?

Yes; that would be interesting. *To Sandra:* **How did you feel about it all? Did you feel bad about it?**

Sandra: Not at the beginning.
   I don't think I would recommend anybody to do it with children.

Why is that? Because you were stuck at home all the time with the kids?

Sandra: Not just that. As far as I'm concerned, Alan missed a year of our daughter's life, and she missed a year of him. You can't replace that year. They do feel it, they do feel it.
   But for anybody without children, I'd recommend it.

Bob: But then again, you've moved up in the value of your house. If Alan did stay at home at weekends with the kids, there's no other way you could get up that ladder.

Sandra: I'm saying that it's better to do it at the beginning if you can.

Bob: It's like Ian. He's done it right – he was engaged, and his girl friend was up here most of the time.

She was up here?

Bob: Oh, yes. We allowed women on the site.

Sandra: But not to the extent that it was supposed to be.

Bob: Women were allowed on the site, not to do work, building work, but they were allowed to come up and do staining and things like that.

Sandra: But we weren't encouraged to do it as much as had been said.

Did Wadsworth's say initially that you'd be quite involved?

Bob: I think they did; yes. A lot of women said "Why can't we be more involved?", but we never had them at the meetings or anything.

Sandra: And with children, it's difficult – difficult and dangerous.

Steve: Children were positively barred from the site.

Alan: We couldn't take the risk of having kids on the site.

Sandra: Barring the children barred the women. What the women should have done was to organize a *crèche* and then they could have been more involved.

Bob: We had a ruling that there weren't to be any sort of uncles or aunties coming to see you. If you're working at weekends and Aunty Flo comes, you've got to stop.

Did the scheme affect marriages?

Bob: It can make or break a marriage—

Steve: —if you're doing all those hours.

Alan: Yes; you have the argument. Because obviously, if you're working three nights a week, and weekends, you don't see your kids and you don't see your wife. It is a strain.

Did any couple split up as a result of it?

Alan: No; but we're working on it! *Laughter.*

Sandra: Nobody did.

Alan: It has happened though.

Bob: A lot of the women wanted to come up here. But they couldn't find the time because they'd got to look after the kids.

The women didn't get anything organized themselves. If the women had all got together and organized it, they perhaps could have done a lot more.

Sandra: Something was said about that, originally, that children could be looked after by one or two, but it didn't materialize.

Bob: I suppose we thought that the men would get on with it, which was right. But come six months into the scheme, you haven't seen the old man all that long. He's just been in and out for his meals, and it's "Right, it's a weekend, and I'm off". That's all you see of him. There aren't many times to chat about things.

Then you have meetings, and they say "What did you say, what was happening?".

Sandra: And Alan was asleep and couldn't remember! *Laughter.*

Bob: It was hard going.

Personally I'd put myself that year aside. Because I'm self-employed and I do get a lot of work at the weekends, I gave up a lot.

Sandra: I don't think anybody's regretted it.

Bob: Oh, no. We've gained on experience, we've gained on the money side of it, we've gained all round. We were also working with eleven other members and seeing how we could work together.

It's an experience not to be forgotten. It was worthwhile, even though you might not have got on with some people.

Sandra: But you mellow about that sort of thing.

Bob: If you know you're going to work with somebody for twelve months, you can't get so that you can't stand the sight of them. There's got to be a give and take somewhere. You've got to say "Look, we've got to draw the line here, because we've got to get on with it". The achievement's got to be the end result.

So you finished on reasonably good terms with everybody?

Alan: Fair to middling.

Bob: The actual end of it broke up. All of a sudden, we all went our separate ways.

Alan: Everybody was working alright until one weekend.

Sandra: That was when everybody got to know about the new prices.

Alan: And since the price went up, that was it.

Steve: That was a major upset.

Alan: It stopped, and it just broke up.

Bob: After that letter came out, there were twelve individual people. Before, there was a group.

And we'd organized to have a get-together in a couple of months' time, but that never materialized.

Sandra: Everything turned sour at the end, mainly because of that letter.

That was a bit of a shame.

Alan and Bob: Yes.

Do you think you've got better relations with your neighbours as a result of the scheme?

Bob: We've worked with the neighbours, you know the neighbours. You wouldn't feel embarrassed to knock on the door: 'Can I borrow this certain spanner'. It's not like with new neighbours that have just moved in.

Alan: I think the whole area's better, because everybody's built their own house and everybody's so friendly.

Bob: They're very, very friendly.

Would you consider doing it again?

Bob: I'd like to build again, on my own.

Why on your own, rather than in a group again?

Alan: We're waiting! *Laughter.*

Bob: Just to have the pure pleasure of doing it on my own. Not particularly build everything on my own: that's a fool. I don't intend to be a jack of all trades and master of none. I'm good at my own trade. I'd like to build a timber-framed one. I'd like to do it myself, to my own design.

And also – to have a better house, to move up again.

Alan: I'm not flitting at all.

Sandra: We didn't build it to sell it. Which a lot of people have done round here.

Alan: They couldn't afford to put the money out to build on their own, so they join a group. Somebody else is organizing it, and all they've done is put a little bit of money out.

Sandra: I don't want to move out of here, no matter how much we'd get for it.

How much did you have to put up front to get this place?

Alan: £251 to join the scheme. For the mortgage, you had to put down whatever you arranged. One or two of the lads got 95% mortgages.

Alan: Everybody had to sign up on the same day. There's got to be no hiccups with the paperwork. We had one solicitor who Wadsworth and Heath recommended. We paid a fixed fee, which was very, very good.

Bob: – About £100. It was usually about £300 or £400.

Steve: With the solicitor doing a job lot, we did get it ever so cheap. That was £1,200 for more or less one job.

Sandra: They all look rosy now, but towards the end of the scheme you could tell they'd done it – every one of them. The strain was showing.

Alan: We were worn out.

After six months, it was telling. But – it's what you get at the end.

Bob: A lot of people couldn't see that, and a lot of people had to be told regularly "Look what you come out with at the end of it".

When we were working on the bungalows a lot of passers-by would be standing there, saying "I'd like to buy one of these". You'd say "They're all private, they're not for sale". So we thought "Well, the value's there anyway". We could see the potential.

☆   ☆   ☆   ☆   ☆

MINUTES OF THE UNDERWOOD SELF-BUILD HOUSING ASSOCIATION

Minutes were kept of the meetings of the Housing Association. Here's a selection of items to illustrate some of the issues discussed:

February 11, 1985

13 people present [of whom 9 eventually finished the scheme]. As at most of the meetings, there was an adviser from Wadsworth and Heath. Chairman, secretary and treasurer had already been elected at an earlier meeting.

More officers were (unanimously) elected: site foreman, and officers for ordering, safety and security, first aid and welfare, and equipment.

Planning approval was awaited for a revised site layout. And a Building Regulations submission was to be made the following week.

Carr's offered (40% + 5%) discount on their window frames.

Facing bricks chosen at a previous meeting were unacceptable to the Planning Authority. So a new selection was made.

The order-of-build of the properties was decided.

March 4

Bob Turton was unanimously accepted into membership.

Licence charges for the occupation of properties built by the Association were set at £160 a month.

Yet another selection of bricks was made for Planning approval.

A JCB could be hired at £9 an hour (with driver), and two footings a morning could be dug out.

All members were to be on site the following Sunday for pegging out and finding levels, and to erect site huts.

March 11

The Halifax Building Society had made a formal offer of a mortgage. Short term bridging finance was to be arranged with the Association's bankers.

Members should draw up any minor modifications they wanted in their houses.

Prices for bricklaying on a subcontract basis, submitted by three of the members, were accepted.

March 18

Barry Heald, of Wadsworth and Heath, reported on interviews he'd had with two prospective members. One was accepted as a member.

A progress board to be fixed in the site hut.

The foreman said there was not enough communication between other members and himself.

April 29
The draft contract for the purchase of the site was near to completion.
The plans had received Building Regulations approval.

May 11
Another person accepted as a member.
A discussion was held on timekeeping. All members were urged to
ensure 100% effort for both evening work and punctuality at weekends.

May 27
Another person was accepted as a member.
Fines to a total of £20 were imposed on members for insufficient
hours worked.
A considerable amount of scaffolding was to be purchased from
another selfbuild group for £350.

July 1
Five roof trusses had been delivered with the wrong span.
The order-of-build was revised.
Mortgage stage payment of £20,000, plus £80,000 for the land, had
been received. Bank account overdrawn by £18,000.
The member elected on May 27 resigned.

July 22
All members were to inform the foreman when they would not be
available for work. And they were to write on the time sheets what work
they had been doing.
The stage claim for the end of June to the Halifax had not been met in
full due to lack of added value on the site.
For more rapid progress on shell brickwork, it was agreed to use
more subcontract bricklayers.

August 19
All members exceeded the minimum hours during July. But the
timekeeper said that certain members were abusing the system and not
signing in and out properly.
The organizer demanded extra effort and commitment from certain
members. He said that he was giving 110% to the Association by
organizing and ordering materials generally outside normal working
hours on site. It was agreed by all members to produce the extra effort.
The site foreman resigned and another was elected.
A request to the Association to provide power hand tools was turned
down.
Another member was elected.

September 19

The outside bricklaying subcontractors had been asked to improve their standard.

It was decided to subcontract out the plumbing on the four-bedroomed houses (£1,400 for the three houses).

The first bungalow was complete and a member could move in.

Fines of about £120 were imposed on two members for a shortfall in hours, to be paid by the next meeting.

An inequity in hours was starting to build up. Some members were 175 hours below the average, and they were urged to catch up.

October 21

Wadsworth and Heath were trying to ensure that cash flow problems did not hinder progress on site.

November 25

A proposal to raise the minimum hours from 20 to 25 was approved by a majority of one vote.

More care was needed. Several repairs had been necessary due to nails going through pipes and cables.

Six occupations would be achieved by Christmas, which had been a very tough target.

It was agreed to repay £100 of loanstock to each member [Christmas bonus?].

January 6, 1986

One member was granted 5 sick hours. [Well, that's how the minutes expressed it!]

A snagging list was to be made out for the subcontracted brickwork.

January 20

Barry Heald, of Wadsworth and Heath, reported that the total anticipated expenditure on the scheme was £325,000.

A member requested that the fines imposed for his shortfall of hours during December be reduced as he had had the flu. The motion was unanimously rejected. Sickness hours could only be credited if the timekeeper had been informed at the time of illness.

A target date for completion was set for the end of March.

February 24

It was agreed to pay the outside bricklayers £100 less than what they were charging (£2,100).

A proposal to increase the minimum hours to 30 during March was defeated by one vote. But it was agreed to put in two extra days before the end of the scheme.

No more minutes.

8

BOB AND

GILL KNIGHT

A GROUP OF PEN PUSHERS
The Sheridan Park Housing Association

SELFBUILD GROUPS usually have a good proportion of tradesmen. This group is rather different in that only one person, a plumber, was in the building trade. Because of their low level of expertise (at least initially), the selfbuild consultants involved, Homesmith Consultants, thought the group would do better building with timber-frame. In the scheme, there were three different designs (all four-bedroomed houses), and these were converted from the original brick-and-block design to timber-frame by Bristol Timber Frame Ltd.

The construction started in the middle of a very wet winter, and the work was particularly difficult to begin with – a hard initiation into selfbuild for a lot of desk-bound people! Despite this, or maybe because of it, they seem to have become a particularly harmonious group. And a year and a half after starting, they had built themselves ten very smart houses, in Stone, Staffordshire.

This interview is with the chairman of the housing association, Bob Knight, and his wife Gill. Another group member, Alan Hodgson, is present for the first part of it.

☆   ☆   ☆   ☆   ☆

What were the origins of this scheme?

Bob: I think that like most selfbuild groups, particularly those that are managed by a management consultant, we all heard about it from an advertisement in the local press. So certainly Gill and I, for instance, just happened to be flicking through one of the local newspapers, and spaces in a group that was already formed were being advertised.

For you, that was just chance was it? You hadn't already decided that you wanted to do a selfbuild?

Bob: Oh, we certainly had; yes. For a long time we had decided that we were going to do a selfbuild. The way that we were going to do it hadn't been decided. We had a couple of friends who'd done selfbuild, and we seriously thought about just buying a piece of land for ourselves, supervising subcontractors, and all the rest of it. One of our friends had done that very successfully. Another one had entered a group scheme, and he was equally successful.

But of course, finding land is not such an easy thing to do. Anyway, round about October '86, we saw this advertisement in the paper, and they were advertising for members within a scheme that had already been set up. So effectively, the consultants had purchased the land and were offering places on the scheme.

We went up to some of the meetings. We bumped into people like Alan and some of the other members, and eventually the group got itself sorted out. The finances were all sorted out, and then we started on site in January '87.

– Not a very good time to start.

Bob: You're absolutely right.

Alan: – And that year in particular.

Bob: I think we've all got our memories of the winter of '87.

The scheme had been going on for a period of months, and we were all very, very keen to get on site. And to a large extent, we twisted the arm of the consultants and said "Right, it is going to happen now, whether you like it or not".

Alan: Yes. The first point was that the road should have been in and wasn't. There was nothing. We couldn't get in, but we still started.

Who should have put the road in?

Alan: They should have been serviced sites, which included the road. The people selling the land to the consultants should have done it all.

Bob: You probably appreciate there are many ways to do a selfbuild. You can buy the land and do everything yourself, or alternatively, you can do what we did, which was to buy plots of land in a group situation. But the road was being put in by the established builder from whom we bought the land. So the road and the services should have been put in, in January '87, when we were due to be on site. He had his own problems, and the road wasn't put in. But nevertheless, we'd suffered enough delays, and we wanted to get on site. So regardless of the bad weather conditions, we decided to get on site and do something.

Alan: Which meant trans-shipping everything by hand from the nearest hardcore road, carrying everything that we were doing, all the seven Newton blocks [for foundations], cement and everything, overland.

You didn't even have a little dumpy truck?

Alan: We did by then or shortly afterwards; we did have a little dumper. Nonetheless, it still meant loading that up from the road, driving it across, off-loading it, and going back. There was an awful lot of work, an awful lot of additional work.

And because of the wet ground conditions, the dumper and people got bogged down. We actually had to dig people out by putting planks around them and digging them out – they were so stuck.

Really?

Alan: Oh, yes. We once thought the plumber was being very friendly and waving to us, when in actual fact he was half-an-hour stuck and wondering why nobody would come to get him out! *Laughter.*

And we had a surveyor and his chain lad on the site; and he lost his chain lad. We had to go and put planks round him and dig him out.

This is because it was so wet?

Alan: Yes. We lost a dumper so deep it stopped. The pulley on the end of the engine actually went down into the mud, it was so deep down.

We borrowed another dump truck and lost that in the mud. They had to come along with a tracked vehicle and pull it out.

Bob: We were very fortunate, in a lot of respects, in having established builders operating around us. And when we did get into difficulties, as any group comprising of people like us inevitably would, we were able to go to these people and they would help us out.

But of course, those were very much the early days. We didn't get into those difficulties once we were more experienced.

The foundations are the hardest part, and they come first.

Alan: Yes. By the time we'd got to the first house plinth, and had something hard, flat and level that we could stand on, it was regarded as quite an achievement – because so much of that had been a 'Mons'-type struggle in mud and the trenches.

How long did it take you to get to that stage?

Alan: April.

– A long time.

Alan: Well, of course, it wasn't only the first house we were working on. It was a staggered development. So by the time we got the beginnings of the first house out of the mud, we were three houses on.

Gill: I remember that for a while there was a whole sea of flat plinths with nothing on them.

Alan: We had so much water on the first three plots that we had a swimming pool nearby that we had to dig for drainage, to keep the water out of the trenches. It was very, very deep. And every time you had to walk around this, the sides kept on sliding down.

   Things were very, very difficult at the beginning.

What sort of ground is it?

Bob: Clay from top to bottom.

   The ground was fine, up until it rained. And then as soon as it rained, the whole place was like a bog. We saw our fair share of rain, I can assure you, in the first year.

Alan: And even for the footings, we couldn't get a vehicle up to the front of the sites.

Bob: Because of the lack of road, the delivery of concrete was unable to get close enough to discharge directly into the trench – this meant emptying concrete into a dumper and transporting it as close to the trench as possible in order to tip (or shovel!) it into the trench.

   They had to come as near as they could to the back, plonk everything into one place, and we had to shovel it round the footings for the first four houses.

   I didn't think I was going to make it at that stage. That was tough.

This might be a controversial question, but with hindsight do you think you'd have been more prudent to have left it for a few months and started in the spring?

Alan: Probably so.

Bob: The problem is, it would have meant a lot more than a few months. We got the road in in May, so effectively we would have lost a period of five months. And bear in mind that we'd already bought the land back in December. We'd have been talking about five months' worth of interest, and having no progress at all.

Alan: Even so, Bob, it wasn't five months' interest on very much at that stage, was it?

Bob: Not so much; no. That's certainly right.

We've asked this question amongst ourselves in the past, and I think we came to the conclusion that we were right to do what we did when we did it.

The reason that I say that is because, operating parallel to us, just up the road, was another selfbuild group. We'd got a group of some ten houses, they'd got a group of seven houses. And they, in fact, decided to leave it. Discussing the parallel situation between the two groups, it became fairly obvious that they were envious of us having decided to get our feet wet, so to speak.

Alan: And we were envious of them being able to watch television on a Sunday afternoon.

Bob: Nevertheless, it did give us a considerable advantage over them in the time span.

Alan: It probably hardened us up. We were three pennyworth of not very much in the beginning. We were not skilled. By the time you've carried a few sacks of cement across very muddy ground, it has a sort of hardening effect. And likewise carrying all those concrete blocks around. So it did have, perhaps, advantages. It was very, very difficult, and you didn't see much by the way of progress at that stage.

How were the people chosen for your group. Did you get in if you asked to be in, or were some people rejected?

Alan: I don't know that anybody was rejected prior to starting the scheme. In fact, we didn't have as many people joining as we did have sites available.

Bob: I don't think we were aware of what happens at application level. So in other words, the management consultants would receive the application forms, and we weren't aware of people who'd put applications in and been rejected at that level. We were only aware of people coming into the group when they decided to come to the meetings that we held on a regular basis in Stafford.

Did you have to go for an interview to be accepted?

Bob: We did go for an interview, but the interview was very much at the first meeting in my case.

Alan: We didn't have one. We had to present our credentials, of course, on paper, and say what we were good at.

You had one tradesman, a plumber I believe. What did other people do?

Alan: Nothing that was relevant to building houses.

They were all professional-type people?

Bob: I was very good at counting bricks! I'm an accountant.

Alan: I'm a mechanical engineer that hasn't had anything to do with mechanical engineering since I joined a tyre manufacturer.

Bob: We had two Planning officers working for the County Council, a storeman from the Gas Board.

All office workers?

Alan: Yes; pen pushers in the main.

Bob: Absolutely.

Alan: So this period of hardening off perhaps did have advantages which we certainly didn't appreciate at the time.

Bob: Being the group that we were – office workers with only one tradesman – the consultants made the decision that we were not going to build as we originally thought, which was going to be the traditional type of build, brick-and-block. They said "Right, we have to make a decision here that if you want to stay together as a group then we insist that you build timber-frame; which makes it slightly easier for a group of your skills – or lack of skills. And not only will you build timber-frame, but we will also insist that you have a site supervisor who is a professional builder". So they sourced a builder from the local area, who in the early days was with us quite considerably.

Alan: He was absolutely invaluable, not only from the point of view of his experience, but also from the point of view of his contacts as well.

So you were paying his wage?

Alan: Not as a group. The consultants took us on with the understanding that we had to have guidance which they provided.

And they didn't charge you any more for this?

Bob: No.

Effectively, they had two choices. They either disbanded us as a group, in which case they got no consultancy fee whatsoever, or they took the commercial decision to say "Right, we will keep you together as a group, in which case we'll be able to charge a consultancy fee and repay our costs. We then recognize there's going to be an extra overhead built into our consultancy fee which we will stand by".

So obviously, they were quite happy. It meant that they'd got a group together, they were raking a fee; but obviously there was that little bit of extra overhead in there.

As a point of interest, were they running the other group as well?

Bob: Yes; they were.

Alan: But because that was a shell-only group, it had creamed off all the craftsmen.

Originally, it was intended to be a 22 house development. Then it got split into two, and the other group had the cheaper means of providing houses: shell-only. And they'd left us with ourselves. *Laughter.*

What do you mean by 'shell-only'?

Alan: The group builds the shells of the houses, and then the individuals finish them off themselves.

They put in the electrics, the plumbing themselves?

Alan: They were all craftsmen. They all had contacts in the trade. They all knew plumbers, their own plumbers, electricians, and plasterers and plasterers-question-mark.

Bob: Effectively they do everything up to a first fix. And then at first fix, the group disbands itself, and they all go their own ways to finish off.

Obviously, there are many ways in which you can do a group selfbuild. You can bale out at whatever level you want to, and all you need is agreement between the group as to how you go about it.

How did you find the timber-frame aspect? Straightforward, easy?

Alan: Fascinating.

Bob: Well, I think that, psychologically first of all, the problems started because we all thought we were going to build what we thought were nice, solid brick-and-block houses. But then suddenly we had the bombshell dropped upon us that we were going to build timber-frame. Well, everybody thinks of timber-frame with the problems that they had in the past, so there was very much a bit of reticence about building timber-frame. And we really did wonder if that was the direction that we wanted to go, or whether we wanted to disband.

Fortunately, there was another group that was going in Milton Keynes.

Alan: –They took us down there and showed us round.

Bob: They gave us the opportunity to talk to the people who were building down there, see the things being built. And to a large extent, that allayed our fears as to what timber-frame was all about and the things that can be achieved.

Alan: Plus, of course, we had the additional advantage that the builder off whom we bought the site and who was building around us, literally, was building timber-frame houses. So commercially, they were regarded as much better than we had originally believed.

With experience and hindsight, I don't think anybody would go back to an ordinary brick-and-block.

You're that pleased with them?

Bob: Very, very happy with them; yes.

So what are the advantages, then?

Alan: The first and most immediate has got to be the fact that I'm paying the same amount now to the Gas Board as I was for a house of half the size and where I didn't have a gas fire and I didn't have gas cooking. And now I do. I'm paying the same in this much bigger house with all these amenities.

They're very well insulated?

Alan: Oh, yes. There's many a morning when you've gone out and found that you should have had an overcoat on, and you didn't know until you got out, simply because you weren't aware of it.

With double glazing, it's a very complete, quiet sort of house.

Timber-framed houses are supposed to be noisier, but you haven't found it so?

Alan: On the outside-to-inside noise, if there's someone walking around with a petrol mower outside and you close the window, it's just like turning him down five-sixths of his noise. It's most muted.

The sealed units help.

Bob: Yes; double glazing certainly helps.

What's the construction of these walls? Is it based on studwork stiffened with ply?

Bob: The external walls are like that. You have a sheet of external 8-ply on the outside with the studwork on the inside, which is then filled with insulation. On the outside of the ply, you have a breather membrane. A breather membrane means that water vapour can go from the inside of the house through to the cavity, but any condensation that forms within the cavity doesn't come back into the insulation.

The internal walls are nothing more than a stud framework. Most of us took the opportunity to fill that stud framework with the insulation material.

Maybe that has made it quieter.

Bob: Well, it's certainly helped. There's no doubt about that.

Alan: Certainly all the bathrooms and toilets were lagged as a matter of principle. Most of us had a bit of insulation left for doing other walls.

To provide for sound insulation, you can put on double layers of plasterboard. You haven't done that?

Alan: We've only done that in the garage, mostly for a fire check.

We've used 4″ insulation batts for all bathrooms; that was the specification.

When we got round to putting up the frames, for the first of each of the three types of houses that we were building, the manufacturer provided us with a carpenter *extraordinaire*. He showed us what the criteria were; how to put each house type together in the order laid down for it; how your studs are aligned through your downstairs, upstairs walls, and on into the roof trusses; what the nailing pattern was – that sort of stuff, in a practical sort of sense.

What is the method for putting up a timber-frame?

Alan: All the panels came marked, for starters. Many of the timber-frame manufacturers leave more to the imagination than ours. We had wall plans, floor plans, joist plans. And everything delivered to us carried a reference, referring it back to the plan. They were reputed to be in two-man panels. Usually it took four of us, at least, to manoeuvre them. There was a lot of weight in them; there really was.

You were putting up one floor at a time?

Alan: The sections vary in length, but the height is obviously from floor to ceiling. The plywood overlaps the sole plate. The sole plate is nailed down through dpc to the plinth, and everything goes on that. And they effectively hook on, all the outside panels. They're all trued up, braced with temporary bracing until you get the joists in place, and nailed. And as each level goes up, it remains braced until you get the next level above to hold it in place. And then the roof trusses which nail into place and hold everything together. And then finally the wind bracing to hold the trusses in place.

How long did it take to put a frame up for one house?

Alan: Bear in mind that we were working basically weekends, and a bit of time during the week. It boiled down to three-times-three hours or three-times-two hours during the week, dependent upon weather. During the summer, we were working a darn sight more than two hours per night.

Bob: I think it would be realistic to say that you could put the downstairs structure up – that's the external panels – you could put those up, including all the head binders as well (which are the bits holding them together around the surface) in a weekend.

With how many people is that?

Bob: That's with four people. We had a shell-build team of four people.

And then another weekend you'd put the upper-floor panels in?

Bob: Well, of course, before you do that, you've got to put the floor joists in, for the upper floor. That in fact, can be quite a big job.

Alan: Nevertheless, at out best, we got up to roof level in two weekends. That was probably with more than four people. That was in the early days when we didn't have people being diverted to other work. Perhaps you could say that with six people you could get up to roof trusses in two weekends. It was really quite remarkable.

Bob: The speed of construction, as far as the external shell is concerned, is really very good. That was one of the things that was particularly good from our point of view. It gave you a psychological boost because you could actually see these things growing in front of your very eyes. It was very much psychological because obviously there was still an awful lot of work to do after the shell was up. But nevertheless, it was grand to actually see your own house just growing in front of your very eyes. As Alan says, in just two weekends, you could see the whole thing just sitting there.

Alan: And shortly after that, of course, you had the whole thing effectively waterproofed. It's a very windy area up here. By the time you had the felting and lathing on, which was probably another weekend or two, you were protected from the weather.

I was scared stiff that first roof we did.

Bob: I think the 'scared stiff' started coming in well before that, even when we got to the first house, where, as Alan said, we had this guy come to give us some assistance in putting it up. That was a windy day. And these panels are something like 12' by 8'; they're like a sailboard. So you can imagine, you're sitting 12' up in the air with one of these being hauled up the outside, four guys hanging onto it against the wind. . .

Alan: . . . and then nudging it over the edge of the house into place.

In fact, when we were off-loading the first kit, we had one panel that had already been off-loaded blow away. It blew over the top of the team that was off-loading, over the wagon and the bloke on the wagon, and landed some twenty yards up the site.

There could have been a nasty accident?

Alan: Yes. The following weekend, in conditions just as windy as that, a panel was blowing away and we were trying to nudge it so that it would hook over the ground floor to nail it in place. It was quite scary.

Bob: It pulls a team of four men together, that's for sure.

But after you've done one construction, you know exactly the direction that you're travelling in; and your team's fully operative, and you do pull together as a good team, no doubt about it.

Alan: It certainly helped having that carpenter chivvying us along all the way. He knew a hundred percent what he was doing.

He was from the timber-frame people?

Alan: Yes. He knew how much you could get away with, how to do it, what to do next. He had people arranged in teams – "You go and get the joists and arrange them in order", and "We want these first and those next".

And by the time we'd finished putting up the ground-floor outer and inner walls, he had a team there with the joists already assembled, and fed us those up, and into place, and bang, bang, bang.

So he was organizing you?

Alan: Very much so. He wasn't just a carpenter.

Bob: In the early days, you can well imagine that a house that comes with something like 40 different panels in it is a bit mind boggling when you see the whole thing spread on the floor. The first thing you say is "Where on earth do we start?".

When the thing actually arrives, it comes with a book of plans. The sole plate, which is the thing that everything sits on, is all dimensioned—

Alan: —wrongly, but dimensioned. *Laughter.*

Bob: Yes; sometimes the figures didn't come right. That didn't help. But towards the end of the build, we'd gained enough experience whereby we knew where to find the mistakes, if they did occur. You can imagine, this having been a computer designed house, it is very specific – all the angles are right, they're all 90°. Everything really should be perfect, provided that you get this thing right at the base level. So the sole plate is absolutely critical.

That means that you've got to get your foundations quite accurate too.

Alan: Well, we did have trouble with that all the way through.

Bob: They have to be level, and they have to be square.

You had trouble with that?

Alan: Yes. The brickies were very much accustomed to laying out for brick-and-block type construction, where it doesn't matter to a yard and a half, because all you do is to follow it with the rest of the brickwork.

But when you've got something which is pre-cut, precise, literally to a millimetre in the length of the panels, the blockwork was not always as would have been desired. We could tolerate up to about 60 mm difference on the diagonals.

Bob: Bristol Timber Frame was the company who made the kits for us.

Alan: They took the designs of the original brick-and-block houses and translated them into timber-frame construction.

Gill: It was quite an exercise for them.

The Knights' timber framed house

So there aren't any other timber-framed houses like these anywhere else?

Bob: No; there probably aren't.

It's a bit like painting by numbers, to be truthful. It looks a horrendously complicated thing, but like most things, once you break it down into its component parts and follow it through from start to finish, it all becomes quite understandable.

Can you talk about the financing of the project? How much money did you have to put in to join the scheme?

Bob: Well, the way in which the group is financed enables each member to put in the minimum amount of money at the start. The scheme is financed by bankers and/or building societies throughout, so that nobody has to actually pay for the house until the thing is completed.

We weren't asked to put in any more than £1 for the share certificate, which we had as a member of a limited company, and £400, which was the figure designed to purchase all the original equipment.

So that amount varies from group to group?

Bob: Yes; it will do. You calculate the amount of capital expenditure you require.

Did you have your own scaffolding?

Bob: Yes; we did. Being timber-frame, we had a special type of scaffolding; it's a hanging type.

But effectively what you do, you budget the required costs for your capital expenditure at the start, divide that amongst your members, and that becomes a figure for loanstock. In our case it was £400.

But that was all we effectively had to put in.

The National and Provincial Building Society were the people who financed the purchase of the land, and we bought that in December '86. As we built, the architects produced stage certificates, work in progress certificates, which were then presented to the building society, and they released stage payments for the thing to carry on. That's a fairly standard practice.

There were no cash flow problems with your group?

Bob: No; the whole thing progressed very well.

Things have got to go really quite wrong for you to have a cash flow problem. You consider what you're doing: You're doing no more than purchasing materials and using an awful lot of free labour to convert them into a saleable commodity, which then has a value which is passed on to the building society. If the project is valued correctly, and the financiers are releasing the money, cash flow difficulties shouldn't really occur.

Where they are going to occur is when you suddenly find that the foundations that you're building on turn out to be not what you expected – all those sort of things which are the unforeseen problems. Then you're going to involve yourself in a lot of extra cash. Then the cash flow problems start.

You're always tight because suppliers will insist that you pay them fairly promptly.

You didn't have any misfortunes like that?

Bob: No; we didn't. We were lucky enough not to come to any of that.

Like many clay bases – we did get to the stage where, having dug down to a metre, we found that it wasn't solid enough to actually put a foundation onto, so we'd go down another 300 mm.

Who told you that, the building inspector?

Bob: Not normally. The builder who was doing our supervising told us.

So we got to the stage where some of our foundations were a little bit deeper than anticipated, but we never reached the horrendous stage where we had to dig down another two, or three, or four metres to actually get to decent bedrock.

In that respect, we were very fortunate because there are an awful lot of things that can go wrong in the building trade.

As a matter of interest, what sort of foundations were they? Were they what's called 'trench-fill' where you fill the trenches up with concrete nearly to the top?

Bob: What we did was to dig out a trench to a metre deep; and we would then fill that with concrete, and that would be reinforced where necessary. We did trench-fill; and then we would use a block foundation from there upwards.

When the houses had been built, did the National and Provincial give mortgages to everybody, or did some people go to other building societies?

Bob: Having built the houses, the National and Provincial then came round to all of us, and gave us the opportunity to take out a mortgage with them. There was the incentive that we wouldn't have to pay for a valuation on the house. But there was no pressure put upon us that we had to take out a mortgage with the National and Provincial.

Gill: There was only one person who did.

Bob: None of us were first-time buyers, so we'd all got our existing mortgages, and most people stuck to their existing mortgagors.

When were the houses completed?

Bob: We moved in on a stage basis, as the houses were finished.

Did you draw lots for the order-of-build?

Gill: No; it was just in numerical order.

Bob: What normally happens when you've got ten sites as we had, you draw lots for the sites because obviously some sites are more attractive than others. We just happened to be fortunate in this group that, when each individual chose the plot that he wanted, it didn't clash with anybody else's choice. So we didn't have to go through the drawing straws situation.

Having chosen our own individual plots, they were numbered from one to ten. We started off building at number one, and carried on numerically clockwise around the system until we eventually finished with the last one.

There was quite a lot of flexibility in our group. The members got on extremely well, tremendously well. Obviously, the group pressures were still there, and over 19 months you're eventually going to find some differences creep in between people, and all the rest.

There were no tears?

Bob: Well, there were some hard times, and there were some hard decisions, and some hard talking. And that's inevitable because you're talking about a lot of money.

Was there bad feeling with it?

Bob: No.

In general, the atmosphere between the group was extremely good – and still is. Now, it is even better because the pressures are off. Everybody now has settled in and got their own finances for the house. We have a lovely street here, where everybody knows everybody and has gone through the same difficulties to get the house that they've got.

So you're closer together now as neighbours?

Bob: Tremendously.

Gill: We came from Birmingham, so we came up here not knowing a soul. We were last on the list, so we moved into a ready-made community with neighbours that we knew, who'd been here long enough to tell us where to go to get things, *et cetera*. We've all used everybody's facilities, from the time the first one was up and plumbed in. It just works that way.

We have street parties fairly regularly. We've had street barbecues. It's nice.

Bob: The community spirit in this road is terrific. And I think that goes for most selfbuild groups.

They do say that the ideal number for a group is round about twenty, and you have a fair spread between trades and non- tradesmen.

We were down to well less than that, of course. We had a similar bond, in that none of us were tradesmen. So to a large extent, what drew us together was our own inexperience. It was great to have one site foreman, who was supplied by the consultants, who was then the link pin for all of us. No sort of chiefs-and-Indians situation ever developed amongst us. As time went on, then the site foreman took a background role and eventually came up only on a Saturday. Previously he'd been here every day we were on site. He'd turn up on site, supervise the work, and tell us in which direction to go. Obviously, over 19 months you very rapidly learn what you should be doing and what direction you should be going in. Once a couple or three houses are up, then you know just what you should be doing, and the time-scale in which you should be doing it, and the sequence of events.

So the site foreman took a bit of a backward role, and then we appointed our one tradesman, who was the plumber, as our site foreman. So we then looked to him, and effectively we gave him *carte blanche* to tell us what to do. We made a decision amongst us that whatever the plumber said was what we were going to have to do. No arguments about it, or anything. If he said 'Do that', then you did it. And it worked very well. We just played our own roles within the group.

Gill: If there were any grievances, they could be aired at the site meetings.

How often were they?

Gill: Not often enough.

Bob: In the early days they were planned for once a month. Sometimes they'd be a formal meeting, which we held in a club in Stafford. We could all get round and discuss any grievances that we had, the direction we wanted to travel in the future, the stage of Planning, and all the rest of it.

And you'd be getting advice from the consultants?

Bob: Yes. We'd certainly be getting advice from them. I wouldn't say it was all one way. It was very much an interplay of ideas both from them and from us as well. They had the theoretical understanding of what should be going on on site. We obviously had the practical knowledge when things were going to happen and when they couldn't happen. It was an exchange of ideas more than anything else, so that we could eventually come down to a plan for the next month.

Over a period, the meetings started to stretch out; we found that we didn't need them. In fact, we went four months once without one.

Did you have any social meetings at all in this time?

Gill: Yes; we ladies all went out for a meal. We thought "How come all these fellahs keep getting together?". So we took ourselves off for a meal, which was good. I used to attend all the meetings because we've got no family, but for people with family commitments, they'd got to get baby-sitters in. So it was great in our instance that all the wives got together, and we found out who each other was. We'd never met all the wives before. We'd met the odd one or two that could possibly come to the meetings.

At what stage in the scheme was this?

Gill: It was Christmas, a year after we started.

Bob: I was travelling backwards and forwards from Birmingham. So I was to some extent a little bit outside the local community. But certainly the lads here used to go out for a drink occasionally, and just chinwag about this, that and the other, rather than talk about site work. Although obviously everything comes round to site work, because it grows horns, this sort of thing does. In the summer at least, you were talking about working from eight o'clock to nine o'clock; there's 13 hours a day, 26 hours over a weekend. And then you could be putting in up to another 6 hours during the week.

Did you have a minimum number of hours?

Bob: Yes.

One of the reasons for the monthly meetings was to set the number of hours you would do in the next month. So we had a timekeeper within the group. Obviously each individual was given a position within the group. There were various positions, but one of them was timekeeper. And he used to look after everybody's individual times – to make sure that they were on the site when they should be, and they were fulfilling the number of hours necessary.

What happened if they weren't?

Bob: Well, if you fell short, you had two alternatives. One was to pay a fine, which originally was £5 an hour and then went up to £10 an hour—

—£10 an hour? That's a good deterrent!

Bob: That's right.

Alternatively, because really what a selfbuild group is all about is man-hours, we gave people the opportunity to make them up in the next month. Money is not what you want; a group doesn't want to accumulate a lot of cash. What we really want is people on site, doing work over a number of hours. So if people fell short, we gave people the opportunity to make it up the next month. If they were still short at the end of the next month, then a fine was levied.

Gill: I can't recall anybody ever being fined.

Bob: I was going to say, there were very, very few fines levied in this group. Everybody pulled their weight very well. There were obviously differences amongst individuals, which you are always going to find in a group. But basically, everybody pulled their weight very well.

Did the women do any of the work?

Gill: Yes. I wanted to be involved. It's something that takes a big chunk out of your life, and if you're just sitting at home waiting for things to happen . . .

So I came up every Sunday afternoon, even when our house wasn't being built, just to see what was going on. But when it came to our house, I helped with all the insulation.

Bob: Generally speaking, women don't get involved in the physical aspects of it, but they were very helpful in other ways.

Gill: One of the wives, because she was at home – she worked as a child-minder – she took on the job of treasurer. She dealt with all the invoices as they came in. They moved in fairly early on site, so all advice notes and dockets went to her. She tidied it up and did the paperwork before it went off to the consultants. So she was quite actively involved. She used to do most evenings. I don't think any of us realized how much work she put in, to be perfectly honest with you. We had a shop business before, so I'm pretty much aware what it was like. She was very competent. If there were any shortages, she'd spot them. She checked the prices, the discounts. She was a very competent lady.

But most of the wives have got a lot of young kids, so a lot of them were not in a position to do much.

We had all the windows for this house delivered to our old home, and I painted all the windows at home before they came up here.

You were responsible for decorating your own houses?

Gill: Yes; everybody was. I did quite a lot of ours. I got corns on my knees from painting the skirting-boards. I couldn't take that home, it was too long.

I painted all these doors at home. We've got fourteen doors, and with three coats of the microporous stuff on it, it's murderous. And of course, everything is softwood, but we stained it up to look like hardwood, like the doors are. So that was quite an experience, trying to find the stains that suited to make them look like the hardwood.

I also assembled all the kitchen units at home. They were flat packs, and if you assemble them on site, you do them quickly. But we wood-glued the lot, and then Bob built them in.

Did the kitchen units come as part of the whole package?

Gill: No. For the bathrooms and the kitchens, you were allowed a set sum in the costings, which I think was £800 for the bathroom, and £900 for the kitchen. If you had anything extra to that, there was a member who was appointed as extras officer, and he kept note of what you'd had in addition to the usual kit.

So you could choose your own kitchen units?

Gill: Oh, yes. Everybody's had totally different. It was left to you, how you spent your money. The plumber had access to a lot of Armitage Shanks stuff, so everybody's had Armitage Shanks. But as far as the styles, the colours and everything goes, you could decide you were either going to blow your costings to pieces and have a wonderful set of bathroom suites, or you didn't.

You can have extra and extra and extra – that's the way it mounts up.

You could just buy the basics within the costings. There was one person who kept to the costings to prove it could be done, but most people had a bit more. It's your own home and you want to make it that bit special.

How has it all worked out financially? How much did you pay for it, and how much is it worth?

Bob: I would think that by the time we'd put everything into this, and that includes all the travelling backwards and forwards to Birmingham (which of course is substantial over nineteen months – you're talking about five return trips up and down the M6 for 40 miles, every week), you're probably talking about this house costing us £55,000. That's with the land, that's all in. That was at August 1988.

Just after they were built, we think this was probably worth round about £130,000.

That's an amazing difference! Why was it so large?

Bob: It's because house prices went through the roof between the summer of '87 and when we'd finished. You have to bear in mind that in August '88, when we finished, house prices were just about at their peak. A year later, to sell a house like this, you'd have to knock about £15,000 off. So we're still talking of £115,000.

So however you look at it, it's a huge difference between the build cost and the actual value of the house.

But that was basically because of this fluke escalation of house prices.

Bob: Very much so. The original valuation was £67,000. That's what they thought the house would be worth, when they estimated a value in August '86.

That original valuation makes selfbuild attractive, but not super attractive. It's a saving of £12,000 isn't it?

Bob: Ah, but their building costs were lower. You have to bear in mind that we put an awful lot of extras into this, and of course, while house prices went up, the build costs went up as well.

We suffered a 5% increase in the cost of the timber frame. And of course, all building materials went up. The one thing that did stay stable was the land price. We bought that in December '86, at what was a ridiculous price. That obviously didn't go up.

There's a selfbuild group going on in Solihull. That's 40 miles further south, in very much a high class area. The build costs on a house like this are now £130,000. But of course, the land down there is phenomenally expensive – £60,000, at least, is probably the land price. But of course, having said that, they're worth £200,000 plus, down there. So the differential in selfbuild is always going to be there. Something has got to happen pretty dramatically for somebody to make a loss on a selfbuild. If you experienced problems with the land, as I mentioned earlier, then that could whittle your differentials down. But if you get it right, they should make the amount of work you put in over a period of two years very attractive. But that doesn't mean to say that I'm decrying the amount of work of work that goes in over two years, because it's a lot of hard work.

You felt pretty exhausted at the end of it?

Bob: You feel exhausted at the end of every weekend. But you do develop an immunity to it. You build up an awful lot of fitness. As an office worker and a pen pusher, I have never felt so fit and so strong as three quarters of the way through this build.

Gill: Everyone's gone to pudding since they stopped actually! *Laughter.* They've put the weight on.

Bob: You're very tired. You're physically tired and you're mentally tired.

Don't the tradesmen have the worst time, because they're doing the same at the weekends as they do all week?

Bob: I agree; yes. I think we had the best of both worlds, quite honestly. I enjoyed it from beginning to end. But there were a lot of lads that didn't enjoy it.

You can positively say that you enjoyed it?

Bob: Yes; undoubtedly. I mean, there were moments when it was a struggle. There were weekends when I thought "For God's sake, we seem to have done absolutely nothing this weekend". There were moments of frustration, or whatever. But in general terms, even whilst I was doing it, I enjoyed it. But I have to say that there were lads on the group who couldn't wait to finish. The pressure of time, the mental pressure, the pressures within the group to work your best for your fellow men – who were always looking over your shoulder at you, of course. It can become quite a strain.

You need an awful lot of backup; there's no doubt about it. You need a good, stable personality to start with. If you're a married man, you need a very, very strong marriage.

What happened to some of the marriages then?

Gill: You become accustomed to not having your husband around. He's not there at the weekends. He's not coming home till half past ten during the week, Tuesday to Thursday. The women have all got kids – there's only one other couple that hasn't got children. So the wife has to become quite an independent person for that period of time. You have to become independent because you've not got the person around that you usually lean on, who's there. So I think they find it difficult then to accept the husband back, to lose the role. You have become independent, and then suddenly you're not any more. I think that's found difficult.

And I think it puts a lot of strain on marriage, the absence during the build.

Did any marriages split up?

Bob: No; there was certainly none of that.

But we did hear from some lads that the wives were a bit ratty. But if you're talking about a woman who's at home with children constantly – no husband to take the pressure off when something goes wrong, as it always does with kiddies – then you can well understand. And when a man comes back at ten o'clock, having done a selfbuild, he's not interested in having a good chat about what he's done for the day, or going out socializing, or whatever. The only thing you want to do is get some food inside you and get some sleep. And you do that for nineteen months.

So there are pressures in that respect, and that happens to everybody. And that's why I say, you need a good stable marriage, and a good understanding wife. And that's absolutely critical to anyone who goes into selfbuild.

You have an added problem for people getting ready to move into a house. Bear in mind that people are moving into their houses as the build is going on. As houses are finished, people move into them and pay a rental to the group.

When was the first one finished?

Bob: It was eight months after the start. From there on, you go in rapid succession because right at the start you put quite a number of foundations down.

What I was saying was that, while you've got the pressures on the marriage while the build is going, when somebody then starts to move in, they've got to sell their own house before they can move in. So what most people were doing was that they were selling their own house a period of months before they actually moved in to their new selfbuild. Which meant that they had to go into rented accommodation.

Gill: Which isn't nice, usually.

Bob: And the rented accommodation that you get is always atrocious. So there's another pressure.

All these sort of things combine to split people apart, if you haven't got a good solid structure around you.

Gill: And it wasn't all roses for the first people who moved in. When they moved in, they had a lovely home, but they were living on a building site. You had timber frames arriving and being plonked on your front – well, it's not your front garden, it's just front mud.

So it might be a disadvantage moving in early? You're there all the time, you can't get away from it.

Gill: We moved in last and had two weeks of discomfort without a drive, and I thought "For God's sake!". But Alan and Margaret were the first to move in, so they were in for twelve months without a drive. That's hardship. You think it's going to be all singing and dancing when you've got your new home, but not for the ones that were in early. Definitely not.

Bob: And there's another disadvantage as well. Whilst we were very fortunate that property prices were going up and up and up whilst we were going through the build (which is a lovely situation), you think what's happened to somebody who's sold their house in preparation for moving in. They perhaps sold their house in April, knowing that they're going to move in June; it probably doesn't happen until August, by which time the house that they've just sold they could probably sell for another £10,000. So there was always that aspect as well.

But now everybody's in, we're more than aware of the financial benefits we've gained through doing a selfbuild. The short term disadvantages tend to be pushed to the back of your mind.

Nobody feels that they've been unfairly treated in any way?

Gill: No; I don't think so.

Bob: Not at all, I don't think.

As I say, we were a very good mix on this particular build. Everybody got on very well and we pulled our weight. If we did start to see something going wrong with an individual, then we nipped it in the bud. But I think we were sane enough to discuss it at a sensible level.

What was the age range?

Gill: Alan's the oldest, in his forties.

Bob: Our prison officer's the youngest, just about thirty.

A narrow age range?

Bob: Fairly; yes. On the build that was running parallel to us, we had a chap there who has done several selfbuilds and he's past retirement age.

Gill: And they went down to late thirties, so their age range was greater.

Bob: But selfbuild isn't a young man's prerogative, not by any means. Whilst you might have the stamina and the fitness, you probably don't have the maturity, the experience to just let things wash over your head, the ability not to expect everything to be done yesterday, and all that sort of thing. Whereas the older man has got that, but he has the disadvantage of not being quite so fit, not so agile, not so quick. So selfbuild is for a wide range of ages, and diverse types of people. It can be done amongst pretty well anybody.

Well, I wonder, because your group seems to contradict that. It had a narrow age range and a fairly narrow range of types – nearly all professional people.

Bob: Yes; but I'm saying if you look at selfbuild as a whole, not just at a particular group, selfbuild can be for anybody.

Gill: As far as the skills side of it goes, from what the consultants said to us, we were the best run as far as the business side of it went. We were more aware of that sort of thing. A lot of the other schemes, because they are all tradesmen and not used to handling the money basically, they were running over budget; and they were paying for materials they'd never received, and the like. That side of it was very competently managed on this scheme.

Bob: We took a very tight rein on the commercial aspects of it.

You had a say in that, did you?

Bob: Yes. I was actually appointed chairman of the group, and as such, I used to do quite a lot of the liaising with the consultants on the financial and administrative side. Certainly that was of assistance to the group. But we were all a very commercially minded group anyway. And we were able to talk at a good commercial level.

What were you subcontracting out?

Bob: We subcontracted the wet trades: bricklaying and plastering were subcontracted out.

Plasterboarding we did ourselves, up to a point. And then we found the work was so time consuming that it made economic sense for the plasterers to come and do their own boarding. It's staggering, isn't it? But we found that the professionals were so quick at it that, when you realized what you were paying in interest charges through the extended period of time that we were taking to do it, it made common sense to get people in to do it. And in fact, we were always weighing up the pros and cons, between the interest charges on a time delay and the cost of bringing in a subcontractor to do it.

The concreting we did ourselves, the shell erection we did ourselves. The tiling we found was so competitive that we got a guy in to do that.

Gill: But you loaded the roofs, didn't you?

Bob: We loaded the roofs out. He actually just laid the tiles. But to be truthful, having seen the way a tiler operates now, I would be doubtful if we would even bother another time to felt and batten the roofs ourselves. They operate so quick, that I think they could have bought this scheme forward and saved us even more interest charges.

You're always weighing up the theoretical niceties of a selfbuild group – which is to do it yourself – against the practicalities and the economics of saying "How much do we want to pay in interest charges, and how much do we want the job done at the right price?". As I say, we were a fairly commercially aware group, so we were able to do the calculations and come down to a fairly sensible decision. A lot of other groups decide to battle on for themselves, extend their time period, and cost themselves an awful lot of money. You have to bear in mind, at the end of the build we were paying interest at £6,000 a month. It's not a difficult decision, when you see that figure in front of you, to bring a tiler in to tile a roof and know that you can bring yourself forward a few days.

Going off at a tangent, did any of you have any bad accidents?

Bob: Bad accidents, certainly not.

Gill: But to a man, everyone was damaged!

Bob: I think we all drew blood on the site at some stage.

We were all covered by an insurance policy that was the normal site-accident cover.

Gill: A few stitches.

Bob: Yes; a couple of hammers went in the wrong direction, and that sort of thing.

But the one thing that we all began to realize was that, if you're going to have an accident, a building site is a likely place to have it. It's a very dangerous environment, there's no doubt about it. And at least 25% of your time – to throw a figure at it – is spent above ground. Of course, if you're above ground, you're increasing the possibilities of an accident.

Things can happen in the most unlikely places. To give you an example, somebody dropped a scaffold pole as we were drawing some scaffold down. It bounced up and hit a guy under the nose – there's a stitch.

Gill: And the same bloke was behind another guy who drew his hammer out of his pouch and the claws got into the bloke's lip – and then he had another stitch!

Bob: Site safety is a very important aspect of selfbuild, there's no doubt about it. You can laugh and joke about it – and we did on plenty of occasions, we used to have some good laughs – but at the end of the day, you should always be wearing a hat. On every day I wore a hat, apart from one day when I was at the bottom of a ladder and a guy climbed the ladder in front of me. His hammer came out of his pouch and hit me on the head – just on the one day that I didn't wear a hat, and that's incredible.

But I was very keen on site safety. You've always got to be aware of what you're doing because it's a super place to have an accident, that's for sure.

Did you try to keep the site clean and tidy?

Laughter.

Bob: We always tried! It's a lot more difficult than it sounds; it really is, particularly when you've got a muddy site as well.

Gill: And particularly when you've got the wet trades in and working during the week, doing the brickwork and stuff. When you came at the weekend there were half bricks everywhere. The teenage sons of one of the guys were doing a lot of tidying up: picking up bricks, and shoving them into dumpers, and driving them round.

I think the answer is probably 'Yes' – Would you recommend selfbuild to other people?

Bob: I've recommended selfbuild to just about anybody I've spoken to. At the end of the day, I think you've got to make your own decisions as to whether you are the right personality for it, whether you've got the right sort of marital background for it, whether you've got the right amount of time for it, whether you fit together in a group of people, whether you work well under pressure – all those sort of things. There's no doubt about it, if you can give yourself ticks on all those counts, then I think selfbuild definitely can reap rewards. But if you fall down on any of those aspects, the pressures that are put upon you can be divisive. It's a lot of hard work and a lot of strain. But if you can come through all that, and if you're the right sort of personality to get through all that, then all well and good, and I'd advise anybody to. Certainly look at it. Don't go into it with rose-tinted glasses; be very realistic.

And that was one thing about our consultants. Despite the fact that they are obviously selling themselves, they were always very realistic about it. They never told us everything was going to be a bed of roses. And believe me, it isn't. There's a lot of hard work.

Do you think the consultants did their job well?

Bob: There were many occasions, in the early stages, when we went into discussion with the consultants about things we would like them to improve upon. And I can honestly say that in every case they did.

What were their weaknesses?

Bob: As they are with most organizations, it wasn't the weakness of the organization, it was the weakness of certain individuals that were working within it. And you can imagine with a group like us, an awful lot of guidance was required in the early stages. We would have liked them to have been on site a lot more. We would have liked them to have explained exactly what was happening in the background. Obviously they went into negotiations with people like architects, building societies, Planning officers, timber-frame suppliers, and we weren't privy to the discussions. And we felt, in the early stages at least, as though we were being left out, and we were being presented with *fait accompli*s.

We brought that to their attention, and we had a serious meeting with them; and all of those matters were put right.

So were you taken into their negotiations?

Bob: Yes. What effectively happened was that I became a liaison officer between the group and Bristol Timber Frame. In doing so, it meant that I spent more and more time discussing things that were happening with the consultants, to the extent of going to their offices and looking over the figures. Obviously, in my profession, that's part and parcel of what I do every day. So from my point of view, it became quite easy to go down there, though it was very time consuming – I was still trying to run a job at the same time.

They gave us every opportunity to go down there and discuss any aspects we weren't happy with – go down there, look at the figures, go over their books of accounts, all that sort of thing. So they were very open with us. I can't think of anything in the later stages that we had any cause to complain of.

They changed their site supervisor, who we were genuinely not happy with. And once we'd explained our problems, they also weren't happy with him. And he was removed off our site, removed out of the organization as it happens.

What was wrong with him?

Bob: Lack of liaison with us. Inability, really, to organize the group. In overall terms, he wasn't doing his job as a site supervisor.

Gill: It was like a timber-frame wouldn't arrive for a house when it was meant to, and you'd find that he'd put a phone call in not to order it. And he had everybody waiting for a house to arrive, and no house.

Bob: But that was down to an individual within the organization; and once we'd sorted that out, we actually had two site supervisors then, and both of those were superb. We're still having discussions with one of them – we haven't wound the organization down yet.

You haven't?

Bob: Well, not fully, because the road and the drives haven't been fully tarmac'd yet. So whilst all the building work has stopped, the vehicle that we used for doing the selfbuild, the limited company, is still there. And while that's still going then we still have a site supervisor from the management consultants. Periodically, I phone him, and I find them very good now.

I would say that, once our working relationship was established, their assistance was considerable, and all members have agreed that they were a welcome 'shoulder to cry on' on several occasions. They were also able to add weight to any discussions we had with the Local Authorities, and this aspect was particularly useful.

All things considered, I would recommend 'the managed route' as being the one with potentially less headaches.

What were the consultants' charges?

Bob: To put a round sum figure on it, they were £5,000 per house. It was worked out on a percentage basis.

Do you feel happy about paying that fee?

Bob: I think that was a top-end professional fee. I've said that to them. They know full well that I think that was the high end of a fee scale in my opinion.

Out of our group they drew £50,000. In actual fact, it was slightly less than that because there were a few deductions for various things – so say £40,000. Now that's not a bad consultancy fee in anybody's books. But having said that, of course, there's an awful lot of work that goes on in the background, particularly before the group is formed. They do have to start looking for land, and of course, they have to pay a salary for a person specifically employed to negotiate land purchases. But nevertheless, £40,000 is a good wage for any man – or any group of three men, which is effectively what we were dealing with. Bear in mind that we then had to pay for our own legal fees, our own architects' fees, all the rest of it. That was purely a consultancy fee.

I think it was perhaps not an excessive fee, but I would not have liked to have seen it any more than that. But presumably, it would be even more today – it's all relative to the cost of the house at the end of the day.

How did you get on with the building inspector?

Bob: Like a house on fire!

I have to go back to the inexperience of the group. If the building inspector came up to us and said something wasn't right, not only were we not in position to disagree with him, we were quite happy to take his advice and believe that he was pointing us in the right direction.

There are other groups that I'm aware of that have tried to short-cut around the building inspector, and fallen out with him fairly rapidly – and quite seriously on occasions. Anything he asked us to do, immediately we went into discussion with him as to why we were doing it, how we should go about it, and if he said "Dig it a foot deeper", we dug it a foot deeper.

I notice that one of the houses is for sale. Do you think that was built for commercial reasons, doing selfbuild as a way of making money?

Bob: No. Circumstance change. The guy who built that house has moved because of his company. Everybody who's moved in here is very happy, and unless they were pressurized into moving I don't think they'd move.

But you said you might do another one?

Bob: Yes; I'd be happy to do another one. As I say, I enjoyed this one.

What part did you find the most difficult?

Bob: In the early stages, the physical work itself was very difficult. We were desk-bound people, not particularly muscular and not fit either. We pretty rapidly got over that, and as I say, we built up the strength and the fitness. Struggling in the mud was a problem. In specifics to this site, not having a road put in on time caused us an awful lot of extra work – just double handling of panels and all that, inability to get heavy goods vehicles to the plots. You can imagine that, if you've got something that's laden with twenty-plus tons of timber, the driver is not going to drive it up a mud lane, because he knows pretty well that he's not going to get out at the end of the day. So they would drop it seventy or a hundred yards away, and we would literally have to man-handle those panels to the plot. So that was certainly very hard.

Gill: I do remember at one stage, when you'd got quite a lot of houses being worked on, that you were spread too thin, and that made all the jobs you were doing harder. There were two people man-handling panels, instead of four. You'd end up with about two people working on each house, and that made the progress very, very slow, because you weren't achieving as a group, you were just achieving as odd people. That was a hard month or so, when we had an awful lot of houses on the go.

Bob: That's right. Those circumstances are one of the reasons you have a regular monthly meeting. We could see the problem developing. It was difficult to get out of it, really, until we all got together in a group and formulated a plan. We decided to drop off one aspect of the work and concentrate on others. Instead of spreading ourselves thinly, we concentrated on aspects where we could progress the work best.

Did each of you specialize in a particular trade?

Bob: Yes; to an extent that's right. Some guys were picked as shell erectors, some were picked as electricians, some were picked as roofers; so to that extent, yes, you started off at the beginning and carried on all the way through. Over a period of nineteen months, you rapidly learn how to do it yourself. We were sufficiently practically experienced in our own backgrounds that when somebody said 'Cut this, chop that, dig that out', or whatever, we were able to understand what the guy was telling us to do. Then you know what's expected of you, and you just get on and do it. But there was nothing to stop somebody coming from one group into another and training. Like you do in most organizations, you try and spread your labour as much as possible, so that everybody's got a little bit of a knowledge of somebody else's skills. If somebody goes down ill, or goes on holiday, or whatever, there's always somebody there to cover. You try to keep your labour force as flexible as possible, really.

Nobody dropped out from the group?

Bob: No. Everybody was quite happy to stay with us.

Gill, to myself: Can I ask you how you've found people have been after a selfbuild? You've been so physical for such a length of time that once it stops – we've heard of quite a few people who've had difficulty stopping. Some of them still potter around with a wheel barrow and things, and experience quite a black period when they finish.

Our jobbing carpenter did a selfbuild, and he said that for twelve months after his build he felt aimless.

Usually there's enough doing in the garden to potter around – patios and so on.

Gill: Oh, yes; there's always plenty to do. It's just the fact that you've not got to do it. A lot of them have found that they know there's jobs to do, but they can't get motivated, and then they feel guilty because they're not motivated.

Yes; that seems quite common. If you leave any little jobs before you move in, it takes years before they get done. They just drag on somehow.
  Do you think people are missing the working-together aspect of it?

Gill: They're missing being a bunch of mates!

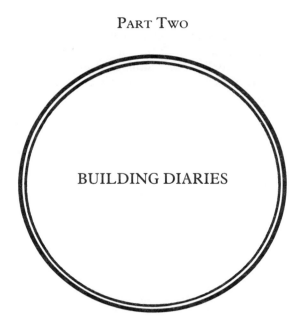

PART TWO

BUILDING DIARIES

WHILE DOING my two selfbuilds, I kept a diary, and very much in abridged form these two diaries are presented here. They are intended to give an idea of the practical issues to be faced, the time-scales, and the costs (though of course, allowances must be made for inflation). I'd like to pass on some of the knowledge that I had to gain the hard way. For example, like many novices, I thought that once the roof was on I'd nearly finished. Not so!

My first selfbuild, at the beginning of the Eighties, was a small bungalow in Lincolnshire. Sensibly for a novice, I used a house-building package. Not so sensibly, I built the bungalow entirely by myself – I wanted to find out if it could be done. I did manage to do it, but only after a lot of struggles.

For my second selfbuild, a few years later, I was more sensible and subcontracted out most of it. Partly because of this, and partly because of my greater experience, the whole build went smoothly, and I ended up with a spacious detached house. I hope that readers who build their own will be able to emulate this build, rather than my troubled first attempt.

During the second selfbuild, a commercial builder built a house next door, and I kept a critical eye on his activities. With profit the prime motive, not surprisingly standards were low. However, I do not wholly blame builders for this common fault. The public at large seems either unable to recognize quality in building or is unwilling to pay for it. Anyway, I have recorded an account of this commercial approach to building to show that the selfbuilder can be confident of doing better.

9

THE AUTHOR
WHEN BUILDING
HIS BUNGALOW

SOLO SELFBUILD

Preliminaries

On All Fools Day 1980, I gave my notice in to the Community in Suffolk where I'd been living for four years. Like many people, I'd long had a yen to build my own house, and now I'd decided to have a go.

It would be very much a case of going into the unknown. I'd never done any building and didn't know any selfbuilders. But for four years I'd been living a life with an ethic of resourceful self-sufficiency. The Community grew its own succulent and wholesome food; our trees we converted into logs and timber; we had an interest in both old crafts and new eco-friendly technologies. Making our own shelter was an obvious part of this ethic. But the Community inhabited a huge, rambling building with plenty of room. There was no call to build anything new. If I wanted to build, it would have to be elsewhere.

To the prudent, it would seem a foolhardy idea. I'd never laid a brick in my life! But I did have some DIY experience. The Community house had previously been a friary. A couple of hundred monks had once lived there, but by the time they'd sold it to us their number had dwindled to a score. With so few, they had been unable to maintain the building properly, so that, when we took it over, there was much work to be done – both in renovating it and changing it to suit our different needs. (What do you do with a former chapel?) So I'd become acquainted with the rudiments, but only the rudiments, of plastering, electrics, plumbing, concreting and slating. Whilst at the Community, I came to appreciate what a versatile and lovely material timber is. I'd taken a six months' Government-run TOPS course in carpentry and joinery. (An excellent course, though since abolished.) So for the carpentry, I was already competent. For the other building skills, I had a lot to learn. And some of that learning was done, as it turned out, in a very hard way.

I've always liked Yorkshire, so I started looking there for a building plot. But they were scarce and too costly for my very limited budget. Then by good chance, on my way home from a trip to Yorkshire, I stopped in Lincolnshire and found that plots there were plentiful and cheap. The south of Lincolnshire is drab fenland, but the north is pretty enough. I liked some plots on the edge of a village near Gainsborough. There was a choice of seven on a small cul-de-sac. The Council had put the road in and intended to build Council houses there, but the Government was putting pressure on Local Authorities to sell land off. The plots were level and spacious, and assuming that the Council had known what it was doing in intending to build there, they would be quite suitable for building on. Water, electricity and foul sewers were at hand. Surface water would have to go into soakaways, and solid fuel used for heating. I chose the plot at the head of the cul-de-sac, facing down the road. Offers were being invited over £4,250 for the 660 square metre plot. I offered £100 more, just to show willing, and that was enough.

As far as the design was concerned, I believed that the orthodox building techniques are unnecessarily difficult for a DIY builder. But I wanted to be sure that my house would be saleable if need be, so it seemed better to keep to the conventional. (Nowadays, innovation is somewhat more acceptable than it was then.) It also seemed a sensible idea to use a 'package deal' – plans and materials from one supplier. It would have been useful to compare the price of their package with the cost of the materials purchased from a builders' merchant, but that was beyond my competence at the time. I had to take it on trust that it was not much more. Certainly, their design service seemed good value. Most of the firms in this business offered timber-frame construction, but it seemed silly to me to coat a timber-framed building with bricks. So I went for a brick-and-block design from Design and Materials Ltd

(D & M). They had a pleasing and efficient design for a two-bedroomed bungalow, and with a few modifications, that suited me well. By using a package deal I would at least be getting the right materials for the design – all I had to do was to put them together! D & M promised advice should I need it, which was very reassuring. They also obtained the Planning consent and Building Regulations approval. This was useful as it relieved me of the need to understand these procedures at a time when there was much else to learn.

To help me on my way, I had Stuart Martin's 'Build Your Own House' – a little out of date even then but still most useful – and various DIY and text books obtained from the London Building Centre. I had been disappointed to find that Murray Armor's 'Building Your Own Home' didn't tell you how to do any actual building!

I was hoping that I would have sufficient capital to build the bungalow without the need to obtain a mortgage. Since I'd be building full-time and wouldn't have a job, I would hardly be eligible for a mortgage anyway.

However, if I came to sell the bungalow in the future, the buyers would probably want a mortgage. Would an architects' or surveyors' certificate be necessary? An old-established firm of surveyors in Gainsborough told me that they would charge £200 for a surveyors' certificate for which they would do similar inspections to the building inspector. I saw little sense in paying for duplicate inspections. And when I approached building societies they said that if in the future a potential purchaser wanted a mortgage from them then they would have the bungalow surveyed at the time – the lack of a certificate would be no hindrance. So I declined the services of the old-established and reputable firm of surveyors. This was to have repercussions later.

Towards the end of September 1980, I was established on site, despite the fact that the plot was not yet properly mine. We had exchanged contracts but the Council's legal department was acting so tardily that I had no qualms about taking early possession. I'd obtained a cheap caravan. (Transporting it had cost more than its purchase.) I'd gathered together the relatively few tools required for basic building. I'd made a trailer, using the back axle of a car with an old steel bed frame for the chassis. D & M had obtained the Building Regulations approval and Planning Permission.

I'd arranged with the Water Authority to have a building supply laid on. In my absence, they'd reburied the end of their pipe, and I had to dig down to it again to connect my standpipe. It was thirsty work, so when the water came gushing out of the tap, I drank greedily. That was my first MISTAKE! The following day I was sick: the water had been lying stagnant in the pipe along the cul-de-sac for years. The account that follows tells of plenty more mistakes. I'm not proud of them, but relate them as a warning to others. There are many more people selfbuilding nowadays than there were a decade ago, and there is more information available about it. There is no reason for the selfbuilder of today to be as ignorant as I was then.

My attitude as I embarked on the project was one of enquiry: was it possible for a novice to build a bungalow single-handed? It was not a fixed ambition – if some work was too difficult for me, I was prepared to call in skilled help.

Winter was not far off, and I was somewhat apprehensive about starting so late in the year. But Murray Armor, the proprietor (at that time) of Design and Materials, gave me cause for optimism. He told me that a 'two-and-one' gang of bricklayers could put down all the foundations for my small bungalow in six days; build the walls up to the wall plate in five days; and put the roof trusses on and build the gables in a couple of days. That was 39 man-days altogether, to be ready for roofing. That seemed mighty fast. How far would I get in the three months before Christmas?

☆   ☆   ☆   ☆   ☆

The Foundations

Work starts on September 25th 1980. I mark out on the ground the approximate position for the bungalow and start clearing the topsoil by spade. A day of this convinces me that it's a mug's game. I arrange instead for a JCB to come over the weekend. He'll strip the site on Saturday morning, giving me the afternoon to set out. On Sunday, he'll come and dig the trenches.

That was the arrangement. But when the driver arrives at ten o'clock on Saturday morning, he tells me that he's playing football in the afternoon and that on the Sunday he's been called away to his regular job. So we'll have to do it all that morning. Not wanting to delay the work with winter approaching, I go along with this proposal. [MISTAKE 2! – I should have refused to be rushed on such a critical job.] He strips the topsoil doing as much in five minutes as I had done all the previous day by spade. There is not enough time to set up proper profiles, so we just put corner pegs into the ground and I check that the diagonals are equal with my new surveyors' tape. [MISTAKE 3! – see later.] We put sand lines down to mark the trenches, and then he rips them out to a depth of about 60 cm. The first trenches are straight and their bottoms are clean. The last, as his time runs out, waver, and the bottoms are uneven with loose dirt in them. After two-and-a-half hours work he trundles off with the £50 that we'd agreed for the price. [MISTAKE 4! – that's £20 an hour, two or three times the going rate at that time.] Although I have an uneasy feeling, I'm pleased with with this burst of progress.

The following day, deflation sets in. I'd asked for a 2' bucket, but in fact the trenches are only 18″ wide. And then I notice that for some bizarre reason the zero on my new tape doesn't start at the end. All my measurements are 10 cm too long!

The building inspector calls by, and I relate my sorry tale. He is sympathetic and allows me just to undercut the trenches to the required width, and to increase the overall dimensions of the bungalow to allow for the tape error. A phone call to D & M confirms that this is no problem with them and that they can let me have new drawings. So I spend a couple of days enlarging and clearing out the bottom of the trenches, and putting up proper profiles.

When the inspector calls again, he asks where the fireplace is to go. The digger hasn't dug out foundations for it. "The bastard", the inspector calls him on my behalf. That takes me half a day with the spade. (When I'd first met the inspector, I'd told him that I was a selfbuilder and admitted that I didn't really know what I was doing. He's said that he'd keep an eye on me and call by frequently – just as well!)

With the trenches at last approved, I'm ready for the foundation concrete. I've invited a readymix rep to the site, and he reckons that I should be able to manage on my own. There is good access all round the trenches for the truck, and the ground is baked hard. It's with some excitement that I await the readymix truck.

The first delivery arrives early on Saturday morning (October 4th). "Only one of you?" the driver enquires – ominous. He starts shooting the slurry of concrete down a trench. "Jump in then" he says to me. I'm about to do that, but he stops me. "Where are your wellies?". It hasn't rained for weeks and I have only ordinary boots, not wellingtons. "Wear some plastic bags over your boots" he suggests. "This stuff can burn." So I do as he advises. [MISTAKE 5! – see below.]

For an hour and a half, I'm paddling about in the wet concrete, raking and shovelling it round the trenches until it's level with the top of the depth pegs. In the quarter of an hour rest before the second load arrives, I clean up my legs. The plastic bags have burst, and the concrete has got at my skin and made it tender. I put on fresh bags and I'm ready for the second and last load.

The second truck has nearly discharged its load and I'm still shovelling the concrete round. The truck driver thinks that we have the right amount in the trenches . Do I want the rest of the load before he goes, and where to put it? A quick decision is required, and it's put on the driveway-to-be. The driver's judgement is right [it usually is!], and I get the concrete all levelled off.

I'm pleased with the morning's work. But that soon passes from my mind when I clean up: the concrete has stripped the skin in a two-inch band around the top of my boots. For five minutes I hose my legs down. My ankles look like raw meat.

I take myself off to hospital. "Oh, not another concrete burn" the nurse says. As she puts on dressings, she tells me of the fellow who was wearing wellingtons, but some concrete came over the top, and he carried on working. He was off work for six months. The seriousness of what I've done to myself is becoming apparent.

A couple of days later the pain starts. I can't carry on working. To convalesce, I go back to my old Community. It's the most painful time of my life. It takes me a quarter of an hour just to get out of bed in the mornings – the pain is that excruciating as I change from a horizontal to vertical position.

But, as Bob Turton said in an earlier chapter, time heals. After a month, fresh skin has formed and the pain has gone. The skin, however, is still very tender. If I were an employee, I'd stay off sick a while longer. But I'm not, and I want to be back on site.

So I return, to find that the weather has changed from drought to flood. The trenches are nearly full of water, a depressing sight. I hire a pump, and after a day most of the water is out. But water is still running into the trenches through seams of gravel in the ground. I don't want to fight the wet weather, so go away for a week to let it improve. Unfortunately, it doesn't: on my return, there's a foot of water in the trenches. This is all dispiriting. The project seems oppressive; there is not the enjoyment that I'd hoped for when I started.

But a small brainwave occurs to me. The Council have put in sewer pipes to serve the plots. The nearest one is not far away, just inside the neighbouring plot. I dig a drainage channel from the foundation trenches down to the sewer pipe. Gravity does the rest, and the water runs away.

The building inspector calls by and tells me that there's nothing unusual about trenches being flooded. This is very reassuring as I had been starting to worry about the plot – perhaps the ground was not suitable for building on after all? He suggests that I get a quote for having the bricklaying done. It's quite a temptation. I could still have the roof on by Christmas, whereas doing it myself would take till June (not working in mid-winter). But the brickies' quote, £1,000, is rather too much, I think. Besides, I want to do the bricklaying. So I decide to persevere alone, at least for the time being. Rather late in the year, November 17th, I start bricklaying.

In the first day, I put up two corners – some progress, but not much! In fact, it's more a case of learning how to lay bricks, than actually building anything. In the first few days, I'm averaging something like 15 bricks an hour – less when putting up corners, but more when 'laying to the line'. The building inspector shows me to lay the bricks 'upside-down', frogs downwards. This is faster. There's nearly 5,000 bricks in the foundations. That's plenty for practice. After bricklaying for a week, I write in my diary "I feel that

I'm getting the measure of bricklaying. Previously, it has been a case of apprehension about the unknown. Now I think I can do the bricklaying. It's no longer a question of 'Can I?' but of 'How long?'''. And after a couple of weeks I'm laying about 25 bricks an hour. (This average figure includes labouring time – mixing the mortar and putting the bricks round the trenches. About a third of the overall time is spent doing this. In fact, at this stage I'm mixing mortar by hand. When the electricity supply is put in, I'll be getting an electric mixer.) We have some flurries of early snow and some frosts, but the trenches are warmer and I don't stop. The foundation walls are finished on December 19th, in time for a Yuletime break. In fact, I've decided to stop building altogether until March, to avoid the worst of the winter weather. Although commercial builders carry on regardless, it was not always so. It used to be a common practice to put foundations down in the autumn, when the ground would be dry, pause over the winter, and then carry on again in the spring. The inspector advises me to cover the tops of the walls to avoid frost damage.

It's rather old-fashioned to build the foundation walls in brickwork. I have done it deliberately, in order to learn bricklaying where the results can't be seen. By the time I've laid the foundations, my bricklaying above ground is looking tidy enough to show to the world.

I return at the beginning of March (1981). While I've been away, George has begun to build on a nearby plot. The land is churned into deep ruts showing the struggles his JCB has had with the wet ground. He admits the New Year was a bad time to start. He is subcontracting, and is already ahead of me with his bungalow. It's good to have somebody to watch and follow, especially as George lectures in building technology and should know what he's doing. I watch as he puts the oversite concrete down. To help, he has nine students! It only takes them half an hour – really a case of 'many hands make light work'.

A hazy sun warms and dries. Spring tenderly approaches. I feel invigorated and energetic, ready to overcome any difficulties. I spend a few days organizing various matters, such as arranging for another JCB to come. The previous digger has left all the spoil around the trenches. Some of this can be used for backfilling the trenches now that the foundation walls are built, but much of it needs to be removed. Heavy rain arrives before the JCB – more bad luck! The digger tries to work, but churns the ground to a quagmire before giving up. Oh, well. . . I take a week's holiday and hope the weather will improve.

It doesn't. When I return, the trenches are once again full of water – my drainage channel has collapsed. I'm about to dig it out again when I have another little brainwave. This time I use a hose-pipe to siphon the water off to the sewer pipe. It's the third time the trenches have had to be drained.

I potter around for a few days until the ground is dry enough for the digger to have another go. He clears up the site and puts the stones into the base as hardcore. It's easy work compacting them with a plate compactor. (It is nice to sometimes have a job that's easier than you expect.)

The oversite polythene is down, and the building inspector has given it the OK. I'm ready for the oversite concrete. Although a 4:2:1 mix is specified in the drawings, the readymix rep suggests that the weaker and cheaper 6:3:1 mix will suffice. I'm happy to go along with this. (In Denmark, they don't put down any oversite concrete, just screeding over insulating aggregate.) Needless to say, it's been raining heavily, and I scoop the puddles off the polythene with a dustpan. Once again, I'm ready to struggle with concrete. George had nine helpers for his oversite. Foolhardedly, I'm alone. It turns out to be one of the most arduous days of my life.

The first truck-load goes into the first bay, and it's three hours of straightforward hard work to spread it around and tamp it down. Concrete is going off all the time, so the longer you take the harder the work becomes. In the afternoon, the second truck drives onto the site but is immediately bogged down. As he tries in vain to move, he digs himself in up to the back axle. What to do with a truckful of setting concrete?

To cut a long story short, it turns out that there is only one thing to do – I have to barrow the concrete across the muddy quagmire. A truckful gives about 200 barrow loads of concrete! I've managed about half of it when a large lorry arrives and pulls the truck back onto the road. It still has half my concrete which has to be paid for even if it goes back to the depot. Fortunately, the driveway-to-be is fairly firm, and I persuade the truck-driver to back down there and dump the rest of the load in the garage base. Although the concrete is getting harder and harder, I manage to bash it flat. It can be screeded to give a good finish. But I don't really know what to do with the concrete in the bungalow base. With only half the required quantity there, I spread it roughly around, hoping to put another layer on top later. [MISTAKE 6!]

When the inspector sees it a few days later, he wants it out. I've made the wrong decision. It would have been better to put the concrete down to the full thickness but over only half the area. £80 worth of concrete is wasted, set hard. The prospect of breaking it all up is daunting. If I were a woman, I could cry and feel the better for it. Up until now, I've remained detached from all the misfortunes that have befallen me. But now I feel despondent. It is April 8th, and the chances of finishing the bungalow by the end of the year are looking bleak.

I spend a couple of days doing useful work – stacking blocks, stain-painting the door and window frames – and I mull over how to break up the concrete. Then some luck comes my way. A powerful tracked excavator starts working on a neighbour's plot. The promise of cash brings him over to mine. He raises his bucket high into the air and then smashes it down onto the unwanted concrete. The ground shakes, the slab even flexes momentarily under the impact, but it doesn't break. The excavator has to have two more attempts before at last a crack appears. After that, the concrete is soon broken up and becomes expensive hardcore in the driveway.

We have some days of sunshine – the weather is magic, as neighbour George calls it. The ground has hardened, and I have another attempt at concreting the second bay. This time, all goes well.

I lay facing bricks to bring the outside leaf of the foundation walls up to the dpc level. These bricks are dark coloured to contrast with the light bricks to be used above. The foundations are at last finished towards the end of April. Builders say that getting out of the ground is the hardest part, but surely few have had to struggle like this?

The walls

I've had to make six phone calls to Design and Materials to get the main facing bricks delivered. They come direct from the LBC brickworks, and it's frustrating having to deal with an intermediary rather than the suppliers themselves. But they arrive just in time to let me start bricklaying on April 25th. For a few days, winter returns with sleet and snow, but by the beginning of May the sun is back. I start first on the wall that takes the electric meter box, and on May 5th the electric supply is put in. Home comforts come to the caravan, and I celebrate with two pieces of toast. More importantly, I can now use an electric mixer for the mortar. This is not only quicker, it produces a smoother, more cohesive mortar. I'm laying about 250 bricks a day. These need more care than the bricks in the foundations; they have to be pointed up, and the face kept free of mortar smears. On a continuous wall I could probably lay about 350 bricks a day, but corners and frames slow progress down. I also start laying blocks for the inner leaf of the wall. The first day, I only manage 65, but since a block is equivalent to six bricks this seems satisfactory for a first attempt. After a while, the rate is up to some 100 blocks a day.

I'm living rather like a recluse. This building has become a passion. I've written in my diary "No books, no tele, no radio, no records, no films, no pubs, no entertainment; nor do I wish for any. No way am I bored". I have to force myself to take Sundays off.

Otherwise I'm generally building until it becomes dark. My only break during the week is to read the papers in the public library and to shop at the supermarket. The store seems so clean and soothing!

There are three other selfbuilders on the neighbouring plots, and they seem to be quite competitive. Their satisfaction seems to lie, not in the work itself, but in how quickly they can get it done. My attitude is different, and I've written in my diary "If you're enjoying work, why rush to finish it. Savour it, like music".

In general, the work is getting easier. The only difficult part of this stage has been putting up a long and heavy lintel. This was a two person job really, but I managed it alone with the help of some tower scaffolding. I've also used the tower scaffolding for bricklaying as the walls have gained height. The scaffolding is inside the walls, on the oversite concrete, and I lay the bricks 'overhand'. This is unusual and slower, but easier with respect to the scaffolding. By mid-June, the exterior walls are up to the wall plate level (that is, up to the eaves).

I start on the blockwork partition walls, and on an easy run lay about 140 blocks in a day. That's equivalent to 840 bricks, so laying blockwork is two or three times as fast as brickwork. But the other partition walls are more intricate, and progress is not as fast.

Next come a couple of brick piers to support the chimney breast. This brickwork will be exposed as a feature in the living room, so I take my time over it. To look right, the bondings of the piers need to be mirror images of each other. The stove will stand between them eventually. Now I put in a lintel to support the breast and cast a concrete slab to support the flue. Then it's a matter of taking the breast and flue up to ceiling height.

By the end of June I'm ready for the roof. Although progress on any particular day seems small, the advances from week to week have been impressive. It has taken a couple of months to put the walls up, from dpc to wall plate level (about 7,000 bricks and 2,000 blocks).

The roof

Putting on roof trusses is not a difficult job for the selfbuilder. But in my case, because I'm single-handed, it is tricky and time consuming. With several people helping, the trusses can simply be passed up from the ground to the roof, but I have to keep dashing from ground to roof level and back again, and to think very carefully how to manoeuvre them. A truss is not heavy, but it is cumbersome. Putting the trusses up and bracing them takes about three days.

From a platform supported by the trusses, I can now build up the chimney. It's a simple chimney, just two brick lengths square, though with a couple of courses oversailing at the top in the secondary brick colour. The whole lot is topped with a chimney pot, which my mother just happens to have spare! (Most chimneys are finished, nowadays, with just a flue liner poking out the top.) It takes a couple of days, and the result looks pleasing. As a matter of interest to other chimney builders, my flue goes straight up, although the text books say that a flue that bends draws better. [Mine performed well enough in practice.]

Another difficult job, single-handed, is putting the gable ladders in position. Rita Blooman, in an earlier account, made it easier for herself by building the ladders *in situ*. But mine are already delivered, so I have a difficult time getting them into place by myself. Then I build the gable walls up to support the ladders. Altogether, this takes eight days for the two ends, which seems rather a lot, but it is tricky work.

Next comes the ancillary timber work for the roof, work that I feel more confident about. The weather is beautiful, and it's good to be working outside. The fascia and soffit are no trouble, but the timber supplied for the barge boards is slightly too short. I get over this, rather ingeniously I think, by putting in a finial at the top where the two boards meet. This not only solves the length problem, but has a decorative effect too. Barge feet are to be fitted at the bottom of the barge boards, but the feet supplied don't seem to quite fit. Are the feet the wrong shape, or is my building wrong? D&M say they will supply some more feet. It's only later that I realize the probable reason for the discrepancies in the barge boards and feet. They probably suited the original design and did not allow for the slightly wider bungalow that I'd built because of the fiasco with the foundation trenches.

Felting and battening come next. I've got four rows of battens in place when I notice a mistake – they are spaced too widely apart. My spacer stick is too long by the width of a batten (because it rests on top of the battens). A set-back like this seems trivial now, compared to the difficulties with the foundations! Tiling in the sunshine is hot work, and the tiles are spotted with my sweat. The roof slope is shallow and the tiles are flat, so it's easy to walk around on them. That's a definite plus-point for amateurs. (Half the tiles were bought off another selfbuilder who had rather over-ordered!)

By mid-August the roof is finished.

Completing the shell

This involves a variety of work to make the building secure against weather and intruders. The front, kitchen and garage doors each take a day to fit, although I should have been able to put them in faster. But they do fit well. The glazing, too, takes a long time, about a week, although a professional might have taken only a day to put the sealed units in.

The flashing for the chimney is very difficult. The chimney comes up through the ridge, which simplifies what is required. But working lead is an acquired skill which I can only bodge. [Prefabricated flashing is now available.]

The Author's 'package-deal' bungalow

A few other jobs are done, like guttering, and taking a vent pipe through the roof. Finally I have the cavity walls filled with urea formaldehyde foam. This is my best building skill since I used to be involved in the business. Ironically, I have to subcontract it out as I no longer have the equipment. There have been two media scares concerning u.f. foam. One concerned dampness, and was vastly exaggerated. The other concerned cancer. Talk of any substance by its chemical name and some people see a risk of cancer. In fact, urea formaldehyde has been used as an adhesive (for example in panel doors and chipboard) for generations, without any discernible cancer risk.

The foam is pumped in through the blockwork. The holes will then simply be covered over when the walls are plastered.

By mid-September the shell is complete — about six months' work from the dpc upwards.

Drains and path

We've been having some good weather and the ground is dry but not hard. While this lasts, it's a good idea to do some ground work.

My neighbour, however, is being stubbornly awkward about drainage. When the Council put the road in, they laid a sewer pipe into his plot, just over from my boundary. I obviously want to connect my drains into this, but he wants me to take my drain under the road to a central manhole. To needlessly dig the road up is absurd. I can't understand whether he's trying to get money out of me, for allowing me to run my drains on his land, or whether he is so selfish that he just can't share an inspection chamber with a neighbour. Either way, he is behaving stupidly, even if he is chairman of the Parish Council! I've read to him the covenant in the title deeds, by which the Local Authority (who sold the plots) have sensibly given all of us rights to put in drains and other utilities over each other's land. But he ignores this. Instead, his solicitors send me a threatening letter. I write back telling them that, if they want to consider their client's best interest, they should make him see sense, not hassle me. And I carry on regardless – the neighbour and his solicitors back down.

Putting the drains in gives me a rare experience in selfbuild – it takes less time than I expect. It seems quite a sizable job, but excavating the trenches (by JCB), putting down a bed of gravel, and laying the plastic drains is all done in a day. Technology has made the job easy. There's no need to build brick inspection chambers – they come ready-made in plastic. And the pipes are simply connected with push-fit couplings with rubber seals.

The building inspector approves the layout of the drains, provided another rodding eye is put in after a particular bend. This is easily done. He says he'll be wanting to do a water test after backfilling, and suggests that I do one beforehand myself. He lends me a drain stopper and warns me to tie string to it before using it.

So I stop up the lowest drain pipe and fill the drains with water. It's just as well that I do, since at the top, where a drain comes out from the building, one of the couplings is leaking. I've strained it too much to get the required angle.

As I release the drain stopper to drain the system down, it becomes apparent why the inspector said to tie some string to it. The pressure of the water snatches the stopper from my hand and sweeps it down the drain towards the Council's sewer. My weak twine has snapped. Gloom! I have visions of having to dig the road up to recover the stopper lodged inside the sewer. [MISTAKE 7! The stopper, in fact, has a small cap in the middle which can be unscrewed to gently release the water. Even for such a simple tool, there are things to learn about it.]

Rather shamefacedly, I phone the inspector to explain my predicament. He comes up with a good practical suggestion: stick the plastic water pipe that I have ready on site down the drain to find the blockage. Doing this, it turns out that the the stopper has only travelled a couple of metres and is easily recovered.

Two soakaway pits were dug out with the drain trenches, and I now fill them with broken blocks and bricks – a good use for the rubble. One of the neighbouring selfbuilders has used land drainage pipe to take his surface water to the soakaways. This is much cheaper than drain pipe, so I copy the idea.

After I've gently backfilled by spade to cover the drains, the excavator returns to finish the backfilling and to scrape away for paths. Fortunately, the digger driver is based not far away in the next village, so it is not too costly for him to come for short visits. The drains pass the water test!

I put hardcore down for the paths – this is a good way to dispose of broken tiles. Now for some more concreting, though I'm being prudent and doing it in two sessions. The first load is a mere 1$^1/_2$ cubic metres, compared to the 6 cubic metres of a full-size truck. However, the lorry won't come round the back to off-load, so it takes me two hours to barrow the readymix into position. I then start tamping it and floating the surface, but I've only done half of it by the time the concrete has become nearly unworkable. I tamp the rest roughly into place as best I can. Another concrete disaster!. [MISTAKE 8! – I spent too much time on floating to perfection the first part of the path at the expense of the rest of it.] The following day there's another similar load for the front, but this goes down quickly enough. I'll have to find some way of putting a satisfactory surface on the paths later on.

Time now for a holiday! I spend the last week of September in Yorkshire.

First fix

The zest is missing when I try to get down to work again. I'm going off to Denmark in the New Year and I'd like to have the bungalow finished by then. That is looking difficult. I work out that there are 18 weeks of work left to do, but there are only 11 weeks to Christmas. I feel I'm drifting, with low energy.

I plod on. Fortunately, the next stage is the electrics, which are not difficult. It takes about five days.

Plumbing and central heating, however, are difficult. They are a complex subject, and it takes me days to read it up. I've had a little practical experience of Yorkshire fittings which comes to stand me in good stead. (The trick is to heat them with a blowtorch until a complete ring of solder can be seen at their end, but not longer. But first coat the ends of the pipes with flux: A friend of mine who is an architect changed the position of a radiatior; all six of his fittings leaked – he'd forgotten to use any flux!) While putting the oversite down, I'd had the foresight to put in ducts for the plumbing pipes. Most of the central heating pipes are microbore and I'll just bury these in the floor screed. [This would be considered as bad practice by some.]

A hired pipe-bender is invaluable, so much better than bending springs. In fact, it's a necessity for the wide pipe that takes the gravity flow from the stove to the cylinder nearby. Quite a lot of the work is in the loft, where the shallow roof makes for cramped working conditions. Plumbers need to be contortionists at times! With the central heating, the plumbing takes about a week.

The carpentry only takes a couple of days, mainly putting in window boards and door linings. (A house would have additionally required stairs and floor-boarding, of course.)

Boarding and plastering

At the builders' merchant, when I order the plasterboard, the assistant asks me "What thickness?". That stumps me. "What thickness do most people use?" I ask. "Three-eighths" he replies. "Right, I'll have that." [MISTAKE 9! That is not the way to make decisions! In fact, it should have been $1/2''$ for the 60 cm spacings of the roof trusses.]

Putting up ceiling boards is another of those jobs which is easier with two people. But I find I can manage using medium-size boards wedged up from the floor with a long T-piece, or 'deadman'. The partition walls have deliberately been left slightly low so that the boards can fly straight over the top of them, so saving a lot of cutting. Boarding the bungalow takes three days. The rooms become lighter and warmer, a big improvement. In fact, most of the work from now on is rewarded with immediate benefits.

The time has come to try my hand at plastering. I've had a quotation for subcontracting it (£800, with boarding). But I've nearly run out of money, so that fact makes the decision for me – I'll have do it myself. It also decides between the two options for the floating coat: cement render, or lightweight browning. It has to be the cheaper sand-and-cement. (Some people consider this better anyway, because it gives a harder result.) An advantage of an electric mixer is that it can be used indoors. I've left the glazing out from one window so that sand can be shovelled straight from a pile outside, through into the mixer inside.

It takes me a day to do the floating coat in the bathroom. It's a small area, but I'm satisfied. I've come to realize that when starting a new technique you should expect to be slow during the learning stage – it's a better way to learn anyway.

A couple of days later I skim the bathroom. [This could have been MISTAKE 10! Sand-and-cement renders tend to crack as they dry out, and it's considered better to leave them for a fortnight so that any cracking can take place before skimming. Although I skimmed most rooms soon after applying the floating coat, fortunately no cracking occurred.] The skimming has come out smooth enough, but it shows up deficiencies in the floating coat – wavy lines at corners and window reveals.

Skimming ceilings is probably beyond my capabilities, so I artex them instead.

As I get used to plastering, I'm skimming about five square metres an hour, but only half of that for the floating coat. And my arm aches. In the kitchen, I brush on a sloppy mix of finish plaster to give a vertically textured surface. It's a lot easier than skimming! (Thanks to the Centre for Alternative Technology for that idea.)

Boarding and plastering take about a month.

Second fix and garden works

The electrical second fix is soon done, a couple of days' work. (In fact, although I relate it here, the lighting circuits were done earlier to give light to work by in the dark winter evenings.) The only mistake was with two lights operated from one switch. They both came on, but only dimly – a wrong connection, easily rectified.

It takes a few days to put in the waterware and central heating apparatus. There are a few leaks; there's one from a Yorkshire fitting in the central-heating pipework. The book says replace it with a new fitting, but I just feed in more solder at the end (having drained the system!). This does the trick. The other leaks are due to loose nuts, which are easily tightened. I celebrate with a hot bath in a heated bathroom. After you've been building for a while, you come to appreciate simple pleasures!

The weather is freezing, so it seems prudent to drain off the plumbing systems before going off for a Yuletime break.

In the New Year (1982), I return just for a few days to screed the floors. Now that I know there are no leaks in the pipework, this can be buried under the screed. [Some would say that it should be kept accessible in ducts.] To prevent corrosion, the pipe and fittings need to be wrapped with Sylglas tape.

We're having some of the lowest temperatures ever recorded for these parts, down to −15°C at night, and the sand is frozen. An electric fan heater helps to free it up, and adding boiling water to the mix also helps. I never really get the knack of screeding. The mix is dry, as it should be, but the surface always seems to sink below the two wooden strips used for levels. The result is an undulating floor.

This is a rather unsatisfactory note on which to stop work, but I've arranged to go back to 'school' for a few months. All that remains to do in the bungalow is some joinery and decorating, and I'm confident about both of these. So there are some grounds for satisfaction. In fact, I write in my diary "THE STRUCTURE IS FINISHED. HURRAY!".

The 'school' is one of the 'Folk High Schools' found in Denmark. Many Danes go to one of these, as adults, to further their cultural education. One of them, the International People's College, caters for foreigners. I spend a most fulfilling four months there, a very nice reward for a year of hard work.

At the end of May, I come back to problems. The undulating floors turn all chairs into rocking chairs, the too thin plasterboard ceilings are sagging, and my money is running out.

Neighbour George reassures me about the floors. He's seen worse, he says. "Put some carpet down, and it'll be alright." So I try that, and there's a big improvement. I level off the worst hollows with levelling compound, and that is good enough. As for the ceilings, I improve the look of them by putting in more nails and putting on a thicker-textured artex. These two remedial jobs take about a week – time wasted, but necessary all the same. My father makes me a loan to ease my financial difficulties.

The summer weather entices me outside. D & M have supplied a large surplus of bricks, enough to build some garden walls and a coal bin. I rotavate the whole site and come across all sorts of unwanted building debris. Wetting the ground beforehand makes rotavating easier, but it is still hard work. A neighbour has some topsoil to spare, and my trailer is put to good use bringing it over for flower beds. I'm now working much more leisurely: only about seven hours a day. This work in the garden takes about a month and a half.

Then it's time to take another long break, for two-and-a-half months of the summer.

On my return, at the beginning of October, the first job is to put lawn seed down to take advantage of what remains of the growing season. Seed is obviously cheaper than turf, and unlike a commercial builder, I have the time to let it grow. The caravan is towed away to a good home, and I (unofficially) move into the back bedroom of the bungalow. Rotavating the garden on three successive days gradually breaks the soil down to a fine tilth. All the stones and rubble thrown up become hardcore in the driveway. Scattering the grass seed is easy and is a reminder of simple ways of working long gone.

The next job, while the weather holds, is to tarmac the drive. As it happens, another selfbuilding neighbour, Rick, is about to tarmac his drive, so we agree to do the two drives together. As with concrete, you are working against the clock with hot tarmac, in this case to get it down before it cools. We've hired a two-wheel vibrating roller, a hefty machine. We put the base coat down for the two drives in a morning. Tarmac-layers are early risers. Rick arrived at the yard with his pick-up at 6.10 a.m., to find 14 lorries queueing before him. As would happen it rains, but we are ready with a sheet to put over the pile to keep it dry and warm.

The following morning we scatter the topping on and roll it in. It's easy with two people!

For the rest of the year, I'm working mostly as a chippy. A month is spent making cupboards and kitchen units. That's followed by second fix work: architrave, skirting, hanging internal doors, fixing the units and worktops, and so on. That takes about a fortnight. Once again it's Christmas, and I still haven't finished. I had thought I'd finish by last Christmas.

Financial difficulties still beset me, so I decide to put in an early claim for the refund of VAT on materials used. Only one refund is allowed, so I'll lose the VAT on materials purchased from now on – but this shouldn't be much. To make the claim, I need the completion certificate from the building inspector. He takes a rather lenient view of the unfinished decor and gives me the certificate. It should have been a reason for another little celebration, but since there is, in fact, still work to do and I'm tired of it, the event goes by unmarked.

About three weeks in the New Year (1983) are taken up with decorating. And there's a variety of miscellaneous jobs to do. With the building inspector out the way, I can put a screed on the paths around the bungalow – their rough surface being the result of my last concreting fiasco. The dpc should be 15 cm above the path, but putting a screed on makes the path level too high to accord with the Building Regulations. I think that two or three centimetres is hardly going to matter.

By the end of February 1983, the bungalow is finished: a final HURRAY! I can start living a normal life again!

☆　　☆　　☆　　☆　　☆

Hindsight

When I first started to look for a building plot, it seemed that I was embarking on an exciting adventure. If I had known it was going to be nearly three years before I finished, I wouldn't have been so enthusiastic. Sometimes it was exciting, sometimes it was satisfying, but more often it was a slog. There is one quality a selfbuilder must have: endurance – especially if they are doing the work themselves.

Putting up the shell, however, did give satisfaction; it felt like an achievement. But I hadn't realized how long fitting it out would take. I ran out of enthusiasm in this stage. I know better now, and another time I'd pace myself better.

More or less deliberately, I chose to build the hard way, all alone. Many jobs become considerably easier with a partner. And of course, subcontracting is even easier. There's no doubt that the most sensible way to selfbuild is to subcontract out all the work. But the project then becomes little more than an exercise in management. The muckier you get your hands, the deeper your eventual satisfaction!

My real hardships came with the foundations, and they all stemmed from that ignorant decision to paddle about in wet concrete without wellingtons. If I'd put the plastic bags inside my long socks, instead of over the boots, they wouldn't have burst and it would have all been a different story. (Nowadays, suppliers of ready-mixed concrete print a warning of the caustic nature of their product on the delivery tickets.) Because I had to convalesce for a month, the work on the foundations was pushed back into the wet winter months. As a result, the trenches flooded – three times. And a readymix truck became stuck in the mud, with dire results. Most selfbuilders will suffer setbacks, but they will be very unlucky, or very foolish, to have such hard misfortunes as mine. I tell them as a warning; don't imagine that they are in any way a necessary part of selfbuild. (See how easily my next house is built in the following chapter.)

To that popular question "How long did it take?", there are several answers.

"Nearly three years" is one answer. In the first six months of this period, the project was set up – finding the plot, choosing the design, and so on. But this was very much part-time – perhaps about a day a week. Once I moved on site, it became very different. I usually worked about ten hours a day, six days a week. I became absorbed in building. When I wasn't doing it, I was reading about it – and had to, because for the DIY builder there is an enormous amount of knowledge to digest. As I finished one trade and had to get to grips with another, the brainwork required could almost become painful. There's a vast amount to think about and a lot at stake.

Besides the preliminary six months, "Nearly three years" also includes a lot of other unproductive time – a month for injuries, three months away from the site to avoid bad weather, four months at the International People's College in Denmark, and five months of holidays and doing other work. So the time spent building was considerably less!

In fact, on closer analysis, the bungalow took only 48 weeks of productive time to build, that is, less than a year. To be added to that, though, is time for office work, shopping, and reading and thinking. Another extra is time spent in rectifying mistakes! In my case this was a month. That's rather a lot, and most selfbuilders should do better. (Many houses need some remedial work before they are finished – commercial builders make up a 'snagging' list of all the jobs required.)

The figures below give the time spent working productively. Notice that fitting out the shell took as much time as building it. However, some work was unproductive, mostly through mistakes on my part though some time was also taken in remedying the effects of bad weather. This accounted for another four weeks, giving a total time to build the bungalow of exactly a year (60 hours a week, every week for a year – the figures are rather hypothetical!)

Here's an analysis of time spent (in terms of weeks – about 60 hours work a week).

The shell:		*Fitting out:*	
Foundations	6	Electrics	1
Walls	10	Plumbing and CH	2
Roof	4	Chippy work	2
Completing the shell	2	Plaster and screed	6
Assorted work	2	Cupboard making	5
		Decorating, etc.	4
Total	24	Assorted work	4
		Total	24

In addition, there was work done in the garden, and 'support' work – necessary, but not immediately productive:

Outside works:		*Support:*	
Drains	1/2	Officework	2
Garden	6	Shopping	3 1/2
		Studying	1
Total	6 1/2	Total	6 1/2

(These figures exclude the time spent setting up the project in the preliminary period before arriving on site.)

Adding in the outside and support work, we come up with a figure of 1 1/4 years spent in building the bungalow. That seems quite an acceptable time.

What is the least possible time for a novice to build such a bungalow? If I had not lost time through mistakes or bad weather, then the actual building of the bungalow would have taken 48 weeks. But this can be reduced further. Most selfbuilders will buy in kitchen and bedroom units rather than make their own, so saving five more weeks. Screeding a concrete floor is unnecessary. It is becoming common now just to float the surface of the oversite concrete. This would save a week. And on a plot with gas available, a fireplace and chimney would be unnecessary, saving another week. Hypothetically, a solo novice could build such a bungalow in only 41 weeks! (In fact, if the selfbuilder didn't wish to learn bricklaying in the foundations, the time spent here could also be reduced, especially by using the trench-fill method.)

So take your pick. You might say that it took me three years to build this bungalow. On the other hand, you might also say that a novice could have built it in less than 40 weeks!

As a further point, I'd add that learning the skills on the job also takes times. Because of my greater competence when I'd finished building the bungalow, I reckoned I could have built another similar one about a third faster, that is hypothetically in only 27 weeks. (I hardly believe this figure myself!)

(The two-bedroomed bungalow with integral garage had a simple rectangular plan. The overall dimensions were $15^1/_2$ by $7^1/_2$ metres, with a nominal floor area of 84 square metres for the bungalow.)

☆   ☆   ☆   ☆   ☆

Apart from the caustic nature of wet concrete, there are two main lessons that I learnt in the course of building:

The first is to work with the seasons, not against them. Don't fight the weather. The builder becomes as aware of ground conditions as the farmer. In particular, don't put the foundations down in winter-time.

The second is to realize at the outset just how long selfbuild takes. Remember, when you have completed the shell you are only half way home, both in terms of time and in terms of money (excluding the cost of the plot). And remember, also, that the building-package companies are commercial businesses, and as such they may be painting too rosier a picture of what's involved in order to make a sale.

Nonetheless, as a novice, I did find that using a package from Design and Materials was definitely advantageous. The basic design of the bungalow was good, and D&M were flexible in allowing modifications. They were generally prompt in their delivery of materials. My main disappointment concerned the advice that was promised, and which would be so invaluable to the inexperienced. Once I'd paid the D&M rep for the package (in advance), I never saw him again. Advice was available at the other end of a telephone line, but that is not as good as personal visits on-site. (The present managing director of D&M tells me that they now accept payments in several stages – much better for the customer. Their reps will now have more incentive to be around to give back-up advice.)

Lastly, I'll mention what comes first to many people's minds, namely, the money saved. The total cost of the whole project was £16,500, of which £4,350 was the cost of the plot and £5,000 the cost of the D&M package. When finished the bungalow was valued at £27,500. Selfbuild had saved me £11,000. (To make allowances for inflation, the average male earnings in 1982 were £7,900 per annum.)

Postscript

I did sell the bungalow three years later. You may remember I mentioned that at the outset I went to a reputable property firm to enquire about obtaining a surveyors' certificate. But I decided against it, and that was to have nasty repercussions when I tried to sell the bungalow.

Gainsborough is a small town, and at that time had only two property firms. I'd engaged one as selling agents, so prospective buyers always went to the other for a survey. And this firm remembered that I hadn't paid for a certificate from them. In short, in their reports they said that my bungalow was unfit for a mortgage. A facing brick that had a crack in it when I laid it became evidence of subsidence in the foundations; the roof, which I'd swept up a little at each end (a good practice with slates or flat tiles), showed evidence of sinking in the middle; and so on. I lost four buyers that way. Eventually, I took the firm on as joint selling agents. By this ruse, the next prospective purchaser had a surveyor in from another town and the sale went through. Needless to say, I didn't pay any selling fee to that 'reputable' property firm. Five years later, the buyers are still there and still pleased with the bungalow.

10

T H E   A U T H O R

SENSIBLE SELFBUILD

Preliminaries

The story starts in March 1986 when I began looking for a building plot near Nottingham. This time, I was going to build a house; I was going to subcontract it; and it was going to take only six months.

If my previous story had elements of bad luck in it, this one has good fortune.

The housing market was stagnant, so there were plenty of plots to choose from. Many could be dismissed immediately. (One turned out to be next to a power station, a detail that the estate agent, not surprisingly, omitted to mention.)

The most promising were a pair of adjacent plots in the middle of a small Wimpey estate. The estate had been built some five years previously, but sales had tailed off and these two plots were left. Wimpey's had sold them to another builder, who was now, in turn, selling them off. Being on an estate was not ideal, but otherwise the plots had a lot going for them. I put in a realistic offer for the smaller one. To my surprise the agent told me that the offer had been accepted – for the larger one! He had misunderstood which plot I was offering for. Needless to say, I was happy to go along with the mistake. The plot I obtained was nearly 40% larger – 540 square metres, a good size, with a 15-metre frontage. Gas was available, and Wimpey's had put in foul and surface-water drains to manholes on the plot. All for £15,000.

However, it was not to be all plain sailing. The plot didn't have any Planning Permission – that had expired. I tried to stall the sale while I applied for fresh Planning consent, but the vendor wouldn't agree to any delay. If I wanted the plot, I'd have to take a gamble. So despite conventional wisdom – never buy a plot without Planning Permission – I went ahead, and ended up with a bargain. A good start. (£20,000 would have been a more realistic price.)

Through the Yellow Pages, I found an architect who said he'd design a house for £300, and certificate it for another £300. The designing would include obtaining the Local Authority consents, and certainly it seemed cheap. We met on site, he took some photographs (in particular, of the other houses around), and I explained my requirements. He went away and produced a couple of 'sketches'. These were free, the bait to win the job.

One of the sketches did please me, and based on it, the architect produced detailed drawings for a three-bedroomed house. Looking at them, it seemed a good idea to put another bedroom over the integral garage, and I asked for a four-bedroomed version. But the result was ugly. So it was back to the drawing board again, this time for the original version with minor modifications. In other words, I was changing my mind, which architects don't like, and for which I had to pay extra later on. (£875 instead of £300!) But I felt it was more important to settle on a design which I liked and which I could build with satisfaction.

There was an interplay of ideas between the architect and myself. He was keen that the house should have a fireplace and chimney, but since the house was going to be exceptionally well insulated and would have gas central heating, I saw a chimney as a useless and heavy adornment. So: no chimney. On the other hand, he persuaded me to put in *en suite* facilities to the main bedroom. That was then coming into fashion and would be a desirable feature should I wish to sell in the future.

To build this house I needed a mortgage, and by devious means this was fixed up. The building society would need the architects' certificate eventually, but to release the stage payments their own valuer would check on progress – yet another person (along with the architect and building inspector) that I had to pay to keep an eye on my work.

In the middle of July, as soon as Planning Permission was granted, I started work. The plans had not yet been approved for the Building

Regulations, but that did not cause a hold-up. (If the inspector is notified that building is about to start, he comes and inspects the work as it progresses.) Nor was the plot legally mine for another week, but I doubted if the seller would know or care if I started early.

☆   ☆   ☆   ☆   ☆

The foundations

Fortunately, there is a JCB based in the village. On a Saturday morning, the digger comes and strips the topsoil, giving me plenty of time to set out before the trenches are dug on Monday afternoon. The topsoil is piled at the back of the plot. One small disadvantage of the plot becomes apparent. Wimpey's had used these two plots as their storage compound, so the 'topsoil' is full of builders' debris. I will have to buy in some good topsoil later.

The building inspector and the architect both inspect the trenches. The architect comes back the following day with his optical level to set out the levels. (At £30 a visit, I'm not sure whether this is an extra or not!) Near each corner, we knock in a post and mark on it the level required for the dpc.

Because they will soon be mining for coal under the village, the concrete foundations are to be extra thick, in fact more like trench-fill than strip foundations. I've arranged to have two truck-loads of readymix with a couple of hours in between them, but after the first load is discharged it is obvious that we could soon take the second. The truck-driver easily arranges this over his radio. There seems to be a good deal of flexibility in the deliveries of readymix.

I've got two helpers for this job – more than enough. The concrete is high enough up the trench for us to be able to work it round from the top – no need to stand in it this time! (As a point of interest, the concrete contains ground-up blast furnace slag. This makes it cheaper and slower setting.)

A couple of days later, we start on the foundation walls. An inexperienced and slow bricklayer puts up the corners. There are several of these as the house has a fairly complicated design. We both 'lay to the line' in between the corners. After a few days, the blockwork foundation walls are ready. (We've remembered to leave a duct through the concrete for the water pipe, and one through the garage foundation wall for the electricity cable. The gas pipe, on the other hand, will simply go up the outside of the wall to its meter box. There's a drain bend through the foundations for the stack, and another for the cloakroom WC. I have heard of cases where the services have been forgotten: it's hard work making ducts through concrete once it's set!

A couple of lorries deliver 40 tonnes of stone to go under the floor slab. It's a bit cheeky, but I have it off-loaded on the adjoining plot to keep mine clear. (The quarry firms want payment in advance, which is most inconvenient and annoying.)

Around the inside of the foundation walls I put polystyrene sheets to insulate the slab; it's a quick and easy job. (I did that on my bungalow too, many years ahead of commercial builders who are only taking it up now because they are being compelled to by upgraded Building Regulations.) The stones are put in place by the local JCB, which makes that a quick and easy job too. After compacting them, myself and a helper put down the damp proof membrane.

After dual inspections, we can proceed with the oversite concrete. It rained yesterday, but the ground is still firm enough for the truck to get round to the back bay. The first load down takes $1^1/2$ hours of hard shovelling, tamping and sawing for three of us. I think that I've over-ordered, so rush off to the phone to ask for the second load to be reduced. That turns out to be a mistake because we end up by being short. I've hired a skip float with a long handle; this is easy to use and flattens out the tamp marks. Later on, when the concrete is hardening, we float the surface off, kneeling on scaffold boards across the surface. There will be no screed on this oversite, so the finish must be good.

The following day, two of us mix up concrete and complete the slab. The little misjudgement the previous day cost several hours work. Anyway, a month after starting, the foundations are finished. It could have been done more quickly, but it's a great deal better than the fiasco with the foundations of my bungalow!

I take off for a month's holiday in Greece. I've arranged that a two-and-one bricklaying gang will be ready to start on my return.

The walls

On my return, the bricks and blocks are delivered, as also arranged before I left. The ground is hard, so the brick lorry can off-load at the back of the plot where the bricks will be out of the way. Some of the blocks go onto the slab, which has had plenty of time to harden off. The brickies, though, are going to be a week late starting. This is a small disadvantage of subcontracting – your timetable is in other people's hands. There's a difficulty, too, with the joinery. I'd assumed that, because frames were in a catalogue, they were available from stock. This is not necessarily so, and for some frames I'll have to wait weeks. Fortunately, the door frames, which are the ones first needed, are available immediately.

The brickies start in the second week on October. We're having an Indian summer (so named, apparently, after the autumns of North America – it's really a 'Red Indian' summer). They start by knocking a couple of courses off one of the walls laid by me. The cross-joints are too wide, they say. They re-lay the bricks with narrow joints, which does look better. The two brickies have different techniques: one 'butters' the end of the brick that he is about to lay, the other butters the brick that he has just laid.

After putting on the facing bricks below the dpc, the brickies check the coursing interval required to come level with the top of the door frames, and then they really get started. As the building grows, I have to rush around to keep them supplied.

For the scaffolding, a firm has quoted £280 for putting it up in four 'lifts', or stages. After a couple of weeks' work, the brickies are ready for the first lift.

A week later both the external and partition walls are ceiling high, and we're ready for the first-floor joists. One of the brickies has a son who is a carpenter. He comes out on the Saturday morning and puts up most of the joists, assisted by myself. He tries out a cordless saw that he's just bought, but it's pretty useless on these hefty timbers, and he soon returns to his small bow saw.

With the joists held in position by temporary battens, the brickies carry on, and they are soon asking for the second lift of scaffolding. However, there is something not quite right, and I measure the height of the joists above the oversite, that is, the room height. It is a course of bricks too low according to the drawings. "It's the usual height" the brickies say. There would be a lot of extra work and possibly some bad feeling if I try to insist that they raise the joists. (I should have checked the height myself earlier on.) So I let the mistake pass, but reduce the brickies' price for the job according to the number of bricks not laid. A little later, they make another mistake and put the bathroom window a little to one side of its designed position. The appearance from outside is somewhat spoilt because the window is out of line with the window below it. On the other hand, viewed from inside the bathroom, it is in a much better position, central over the wash basin. I'm quite happy to go along with this 'modification'. A fortnight after the joisting, the brickies reach the wall plate. We haven't sorted out beforehand whether or not this is included in their price, so I bed it on – an easy job.

The roof

There is now a problem. The roof trusses arrived a fortnight ago, in plenty of time. Unfortunately, the rafter ends of eight of them have been crushed by the wheel of a lorry. It took six weeks to have the trusses made up. Will it take another six weeks to get some replacements?

I phone the builders' merchants whose lorry must have done the damage – the only one that has come on site while the trusses have been there. They take a high-handed attitude and say that, as no-one actually saw the accident happen and their lorry driver denies doing it, then they will not consider any compensation to me. However, I owe them money for goods supplied, and I simply reduce my payment to them by £50. That, though, is not to be the end of the story.

Meanwhile, I realize that Fortune smiles on me. The house has an L-shaped plan, which means that some trusses are supported at one end, not by a wall, but by another extra strong truss. These particular trusses need a rafter end to be cut off where they join the supporting truss. And it so happens that eight of these trusses are required, precisely the number with damaged ends. So I cut the damaged ends off, and work proceeds.

We're now into the middle of November, but on the day for putting up the trusses we have perfect weather, fine and still. Three of us get most of the trusses up in the day. A few days later the brickies return to put up the gables. The gables are supported at their ends by brick corbels. The verges have a couple of courses on the slope, oversailing the brickwork below. The brickies, experienced though they are, seem to find it quite tricky how to put it all this together. Like much else in building, it seems simple once it's in place, but not before.

On one of the gables the brickies have a mishap. They take the inner leaf up rather too high above the supporting outer leaf. A sudden gust of wind blows the green blockwork down to the ground. Fortunately, the only damage done is to blocks and bricks, not to anyone's head!

Their work completed, I pay off the brickies. By agreement I've been keeping a little behind with their weekly payments, so there is a bonus for them now that they've finished. Overall they've done a good job, despite mistakes. The architect did send me a letter saying that the bricklayers should work more cleanly, but I imagine that this is a common complaint from architects. The leader of the little gang, Sam, has the independent air of the journeyman/craftsman. He is happy to discourse about politics, religion, or any issue of the day.

Some time previously, a roofer had called by and asked to be allowed to put a quote in. The price was keen, not a lot more than I would have had to pay just for materials, so he's got the job. It is, in fact, a small family firm. One of the sons does flashing – it seems sensible to me for roofers to do this rather than plumbers. Felting and battening, and then tiling the roof of the house takes just a few days. At the valleys, they take away the valley boards that I'd laid, and put down fibreglass mouldings. These are another of the technical innovations that make building faster and easier.

Before the scaffolding is stripped, it's sensible to use it to do some jobs high up. I stain-paint the exposed rafter ends. (The eaves are in a 'cottage' style.) My neighbour has allowed some of my scaffolding to be put on his land, so to show goodwill I also paint the woodwork of his house that is accessible from the scaffolding. (I was surprised that the planners allowed me to put my house so close to his!) Lastly, I put round the guttering, so easy to do from scaffolding.

The scaffolding is stripped to reveal a good-looking house. The shape is pleasing, and the two differently coloured bricks that it's built with look well together.

I build up the porch roof. The architect has specified a thick oak post to support it, but there doesn't seem to be any seasoned oak available locally. Eventually I track down an elm post for only £5. That does the job well.

The porch roof is a continuation of the garage roof; once the trusses have been put on for that, the tiler returns to tile them both.

Completing the shell

Nearly all the windows are to have sealed units, with one pane in low-emissive ('low-e') glass. Quotations for the units vary widely. The price differences cannot be justified at all in terms of differences of material or labour costs. Some firms are aiming at the replacement double-glazing market, selling an 'image' more than glass, and their prices are excessive. Fortunately, other firms are producing sealed units as just another component for the building industry, and their prices are much lower.

The Author's architect - designed house

When I collect the sealed units, the firm tells me to put the pane of low-e glass on the outside. I have doubts, however, about this and phone the manufacturers of the glass. As I thought, the low-e pane should be on the inside.

It takes me a morning to put in a couple of units. Too slow! It's time to call in the professionals. In a morning, two of them put in 21 units – they each glaze five times as fast as I can.

With external doors on, the shell can be secured for the Yuletime break.

The drains

The New Year is hardly the time to get involved with drains, but the weather is mild and dry, and there's a digger working nearby willing to come over for an hour or two. Having the house connected to drains will definitely make for more convenience! So I decide to go ahead.

Before starting on the trenches, I get the digger to strip an area for the patio at the back. I haven't thought earlier about how big to make this, so I have to make a rather arbitrary decision off the top of my head. This is happening rather too much: I have to make impromptu decisions with long-lasting consequences. It happens when I haven't had the time or vision to see all the eventual detail of the whole.

This digger driver is very experienced. I have only to explain the layout of the drains and that's enough for him. He doesn't need lines marked on the ground, and the falls he gauges by eye. Unfortunately, I forget to warn him about the phone wire put in earlier, and he rips this up. (Happily, British Telecom give a free replacement later.)

The next day, myself and helper lay most of the drains – in clayware this time, so they don't need any gravel around them. The architect has specified several new manholes and back inlet gullies. They seem excessive to me. Instead of three manholes, I put in a rodding eye and two access chambers – easier and cheaper. And where the downpipes from the gutters run into the drains, I just put in bends instead of gullies. Gullies contain a water trap and seal off the drain, but there is no need for that with the surface-water drain.

It takes us three days to break into the two existing manholes (put in by Wimpey's) and to lay the drains. It's starting to snow. When the building inspector visits, he notices that we've completely forgotten the drain from one of the downpipes!

Before we can lay this, the snow comes down more thickly, until it is lying nearly a foot deep. It's time to become an office worker! So for a week, I turn my attention to paperwork and general managerial matters.

The snow clears, and I finish off the drains. I partly backfill the trenches by spade so that the pipes are covered. (Otherwise, the rougher backfilling done by a digger can crack the drains.) A few days later, the JCB returns to spend an hour finishing off the backfilling and clearing the site generally.

First fix

Towards the end of January, Malcolm the plumber starts the work inside. Despite his rather laconic attitude, Malcolm turns out to be an ideal tradesman: knowledgeable, hardworking, intelligent and conscientious. He identifies the positions for all the appliances and then works out the pipe runs. The only one that gives difficulty is the waste from the *en suite* – it has too long a run to keep a fall on it. But then he decides to take the stack up into the loft via the cylinder cupboard – a better position for it anyway – and the problem is solved.

I've left ducts in the ground-floor slab to take the pipework for the ground floor, but Malcolm doesn't want to use them. Instead, he puts the pipework in the upper-floor void, with drops down the walls in microbore for the ground-floor radiators. In less than a week, Malcolm has finished; he has done a very professional job.

With the pipework in place, I can carry on boarding the upper floor. With tongue-and-grooved chipboard, this is an easy enough job, though it does take me several days. (Water-resistant board is used in the bathroom and *en suite* areas.) After that comes the studwork. This is another easy job, at least when the right technique is used: make it up flat on the floor, not *in situ*.

To finish off the carpentry, I put in the door linings and window boards. Because the wall cavity is wider than normal, it is difficult to find wide enough window boards in natural wood. Most of the wide window boards are made from artificial board. After a lot of phone work, I eventually locate some boards in parana pine, which will look fine when varnished.

' Stairs should be fitted before plastering. Mine are very difficult to make. Because they have to fit into a very constrained space, they have two sets of winders. A local joiner said that he could make them. But after several weeks, he still hadn't found the time even to give me a price. Some people just don't know when to say 'No'. After wasting time with him, I've taken my order elsewhere. But as a result, the stairs will not be ready until after plastering.

The electrician comes in for a week. This is quite straightforward work, except that we both forget about the central-heating wiring. Fortunately, I remember before plastering, and put a three-core-and-earth cable between the boiler and the cylinder cupboard.

Also before plastering, I put in TV and FM cables, and wires for the phone extensions and door bell. It's easy enough to do, and they will be much neater buried under the plaster.

Boarding and plastering

Plasterers usually do the boarding as well as plastering, but it's not particularly skilled work. Myself and a helper put up the ceiling boards. It becomes apparent that I've made a mistake with the spacing of the trusses. They're all spaced out evenly, but at a little less than 60 cm. If they had been fixed at exactly 60 cm centres, the plasterboards (of length 120 cm) would not need cutting. That sort of foresight needs experience and is difficult for the selfbuilder.

I've engaged a large firm for the plastering, so it's a little surprising when they send along only one man, Mick. But he soon proves himself a very capable worker.

He starts off skimming the ceilings upstairs. He is just in time, because the boards have been up for more than a week in damp weather and are just starting to sag. For scrimming over the joints between the boards he uses a self-adhesive nylon scrim – yet another technical advance that makes the job easier and quicker.

With the ceilings skimmed, Mick turns his attention to the walls upstairs. He starts off by knocking off all the 'claggs'. These are pieces of mortar which have been squeezed out from the joints while the blockwork was being laid, and which would stick out through the plaster. As he knocks off the claggs, Mick curses bricklayers – a ritual, I suspect, that he frequently goes through.

He also complains that he has to rush all the time, working to a price. No-one cares, he says, about the quality. He'd rather be on day work, but that would be too much of a drop in money. On this job, he's making about £5 an hour. The cost of plastering is £1,100 (with plasterboard fixed by me). A break-down of this price is interesting. One third is going to Mick's wages, one third is the cost of the materials, and the remaining third is for the firm's overheads and profits. Their price was the best I could get. Mick tells me that another time, he and his mates could do the job, more cheaply, over a couple of weekends.

Anyway, for this job at present, he uses browning for the floating coat which can be skimmed only a few hours after being applied. That way the job progresses quickly, although it is hard graft for him. Within a fortnight, Mick has plastered the house single-handed. He has done quite a good job, though it's certainly not excellent. Putting a metre-long straight edge up against the walls frequently shows hollows to a depth of half a centimetre.

A few days later, a pair of artexers come to do the lounge ceiling. First of all, they tape over the joints between the boards. The following day, when the compound has hardened, they return to texture the ceiling. One person puts the compound on, the other follows close behind texturing it before it stiffens. They demonstrate a variety of patterns to me, and I select 'broken leather'. The quite large ceiling takes the pair of them only an hour.

Garden works

It's the end of March, and with spring coming in, I'm tempted outside.

Broken bricks and blocks have been put down as hardcore for paths and patios, and these are now concreted over. The paths are finished off by drawing a stiff broom across the surface to give a 'cordroy' effect – easy and quite attractive.

The front and back patios are rather more special. For each of them, I first put down a concrete base. Then I cast 'slabs' *in situ*, using a thin screed straight onto the concrete. The slabs are cast, in fact, in a square or octagonal mould set in the required position. By using differently coloured aggregates, and white as well as grey cement, a variety of different looking 'slabs' are obtained. The overall effect is interesting and distinctive. It has been something of an experiment, but I'm well pleased with the result: a pair of patios that are more attractive and much cheaper than those made with the manufactured square slabs.

Second fix

After a week or so in the garden, I return inside to make the cupboards and drawers for the kitchen and utility room. When I made these for the bungalow they were based on a traditional framework. This time I use the modern technique of just screwing plastic-coated chipboard together. It's certainly faster.

With the cupboards made, I can now turn my attention to the second fix work. The cupboards are fitted, and the dining room is clad all round in pine matching. The cladding is easy to do, is not expensive (especially as the cost of plastering the walls is saved), and will be much admired later.

At last the staircase arrives, in four parts. Trying first of all a dry run, two of us screw and wedge the whole staircase together. With two turns in it, the staircase is a cumbersome structure. And then, with a lot of trying, we manoeuvre it into its very restricted space. Stairs either fit, or they don't. These do. Reassured, we take the staircase apart and then re-assemble it using glue. Once again we put the staircase into place, and this time screw the strings to the walls. To make a neat job, the walls here have been left unplastered. They can be plastered over later. (It is, of course, much better to fit the staircase before any plastering.)

The story of the broken roof trusses is now continued. The builders' merchants, whose lorry very probably broke their ends, has not accepted my keeping back £50 for compensation. Their solicitors summons me to the Small Claims Court. But at the preliminary hearing, the arbitrator is obviously sympathetic to my case, and a few days later the solicitors withdraw the case – a silly storm in a teacup.

Back to more productive work.

I fit the balanced-flue gas fire in the lounge. The large circular hole through the wall, for the flue, is easily chain drilled out. Balanced flues for boilers have been around for years. Extending the principle to gas fires saves the need to build a flue up the wall. Malcolm returns to connect up the fire and do the rest of the second fix plumbing. He has a little accident while screwing down the lavatory pan in the cloakroom. He screws too tightly, and for the first time in his career cracks a pan.

The electrician needs only a couple of days for the second fix. At the end, he collects up all the offcuts of cable. He reckons they're worth £5 from a scrap dealer.

Meanwhile, I carry on doing a mixture of decorating and chippying. It's now June, and I'm getting bored with finishing off the house. But decorating the hall and landing brings some renewed interest as I print patterns over the walls with carpet dies. (A 'die' is a shape cut out of old carpet and stuck onto a piece of board. With the carpet wetted with paint, the die can be dabbed repeatedly onto the wall to give a pattern. It's simple and effective.)

The DIY builder can work as the logic of the jobs requires, putting on whichever tradesman's hat is appropriate. Decorating the stairwell is a case in point. In commercial work, decorating is usually left until last, but in my case it is much easier to paint the stairwell before the balusters are put up. So I paint the stairwell, then put my carpenter's apron back on and fit the balusters. These are now being marketed in kit form for the DIY market. It is not too difficult a job – though a novice wouldn't find it easy either.

I carry on hanging internal doors. These take me nearly two hours a door, but this is not much more than Spon's Architects' and Builders' Price Book gives for the time of a professional. The doors are described as 'hardwood', that is, hardwood veneers on soft-wood cores – imitation, but more ecological than using solid tropical hardwood.

The electricity company comes to replace their temporary supply with the permanent one. The gas supply is also connected. I had a pleasant surprise when I applied for this: Wimpey's had already paid for the connection. In fact, because Wimpey's had had to pay to bring gas to the estate, it had cost them about £1,000 a plot – a substantial sum.

With the gas and electricity connected, Malcolm returns to commission the central heating system. "Nice ceilings" he says laconically, as he fills the system up to check for leaks. And nice ceilings they stay – no leaks!

It's now July, and I'm putting up architrave. In a day I put up 12 sets of architrave, which is about the rate that Spon's Price Book gives for a tradesman. With the architraving in place, I go along with convention downstairs and put round skirting. (I don't bother with it upstairs.) Once again, as a DIY builder I can make work easier overall by giving the architrave and skirting a coat of paint before putting it in place.

From mid-July, there's a three month period when I do little more to the house – most of the time I'm abroad on a working holiday in Denmark. But don't think I'm a workaholic. There is also a couple of weeks in Malta, taking it very easy.

On my return, a week is spent making drawers and doors for my kitchen and utility units. Altogether, it has taken a month to make 18 units, and the material has cost £500. The cost of buying in comparable units might have been about £900. It's questionable whether the money saved is worth the month's delay in finishing the house. On the other hand, I have enjoyed making them. "Am I working or playing?" is a question I've often asked myself while selfbuilding. And the units do give an individual style to the kitchen. Whether to make or buy kitchen units is part of a general dilemma in selfbuild. You can pay out money and get the house built quickly, or you can save money and do it yourself. Somewhere there is an economic optimum, and this differs for different people in different circumstances. (And of course, economic factors are not the only ones.)

A couple of weeks are spent doing sundry little jobs, and then at the beginning of November the house is ready for inspection. The building inspector spends about five minutes looking round. He notices a downpipe has slipped down, but otherwise he is satisfied. The completion certificate will be on its way. The architect is somewhat more fussy, though not unreasonably so. He notices that the porch roof is starting to sag, and the reason for this is that I've put in a beam which is much smaller than he specified: it will have to be reinforced. The other points are more minor, such as sealing with mastic the cracks between brickwork and frames. He is still dubious about my drains. However, the building inspector has approved them, so he will too. Going round with the architect, I see with fresh eyes all the little jobs that I haven't quite finished. Lastly, the valuer comes round for the Halifax Building Society. He seems to like what he sees.

The greater part of November is taken up with numerous little jobs: tiling in the bathroom and kitchen, rag rolling some walls (delightfully easy), diverse remedial work, and so on. By the end of the month, the carpeting has been fitted, and the house is ready for occupation.

☆　　☆　　☆　　☆　　☆

Hindsight

I set out to build a house in six months. I failed, in that it took a good deal longer than that. But I did succeed on a more important point – the house did get built. And it's a fine house, admired by many.

From beginning to end, the construction process took 16 months. However, for four of these months I was away, so that effectively the work took a year. Compared to my solo labours on the bungalow, it was an easy year. Much of the time, I could just leave the subcontractors to get on with it. Overall, I was probably putting in a thirty-hour week.

Altogether, it was a more ordinary experience than my first build. There were no significant setbacks. Using subcontractors obviously makes the job much easier. Moreover, it was my second selfbuild. The first had been an adventure into the unknown. For the second, I was in what was now familiar territory, and some luck came my way.

It would have been quite possible to build the house much quicker by subcontracting all the labour. As it was, the roof was on in only three-and-a-half months. This included a month for the foundations, which, with professional labour, could have been done in half the time. A lot more time could have been saved in the fitting out. I did a good proportion of this, and I'm slow and there's only one of me. I did the carpentry work, the decorating, and, with some assistance, the plasterboarding. A month was spent making cupboards, which normally would be bought in. (Three weeks was spent on drains and garden works. On this plot there were no boundary walls or fences to build – as it happens, all the boundary fences belong to neighbours.) Bearing these points in mind, it would seem not unreasonable to say that the house could have been fitted out in only three months.

So if time had been the priority, the house could have been built fairly easily in only six months.

The costs

The table gives a break-down of the costs involved. For work which I did myself, I have put the labour cost that would have been incurred if the work had been subcontracted.

(The spacious house has three double bedrooms and has an integral garage. The external walls are: brick – 6 cm insulation batts – block. The partition walls downstairs are in blockwork, and upstairs they are studwork covered with doubled sheets of plasterboard. The roofs are trusses covered with concrete pantiles. The nominal floor area of the house is 130 square metres.)

The table shows that the overall building cost was £30,000. The house has a nominal floor area of 130 square metres giving £231 as the building cost per square metre of floor.

Spon's Price Book contains, amongst masses of other figures, an approximate cost figure for building a detached house with central

Costs involved in building the author's house

	Materials £	Labour £	Total £	Main items
Shell:				
Foundations	1,700	600	2,300	Concrete – £840
				Aggregate – £320
				Blocks – £300
Walls	5,700	3,200	8,900	Bricks – £1,900
				Blocks – £1,100
				Frames – £1,000
				Lintels – £600
				Joists – £300
				Sand – £200
				Insulation – £200
Roof	1,900	400	2,300	Trusses – £650
				Tiles – £500
				Felt & battens – £500
Shell completion	1,700	150	1,850	Glazing – £600
				External doors – £600
Subtotal:	11,000	4,350	15,350	
Fitting out:				
First Fix:				
Plumbing	300	200	500	
Electrics	400	250	650	
Carpentry	1,000	450	1,450	Staircase – £450
				Flooring – £250
Plaster & board	800	1,200	2,000	Plasterboard – £450
Second Fix:				
Plumbing	1,900	400	2,300	
Electrics	300	250	550	
Carpentry	1,000	400	1,500	Balusters – £300
				Internal doors – £250
Decorating	300	700	1,000	
Cupboards	500	400	900	
Fitting out	900	100	1,000	
Subtotal:	7,400	4,350	11,850	
Drains	500	300	800	
Garden	500	500	1,000	Turf – £200
TOTAL	19,400	9,600	29,000	

Extras:
excavator costs – £380
scaffolding hire – £250
tool hire – £130
phone – £70
van petrol – £170 (say)
Total extras – £1,000

[The labour costs (£9,600) break down as follows:

subcontracted labour – £6,000
direct labour – £450
Estimated value of my labour – £3,150
(for manual work, not managerial!)]

Overall building cost – £30,000

heating. The 1987 edition gives a figure of £380 – £480 per square metre of nominal floor area. This is much greater than both my cost (above) and the cost of the commercially-built house of the next chapter. Although Spon's prices include a 6% to 12% increment to cover overheads and profits, it is something of a mystery to me why they are so much higher. In Spon's own words: "The prices must be treated with reserve". The prospective selfbuilder need not be dismayed nor deterred by their high figures.

Fees came to £1,800 (for design, inspections and service connections). The cost of the plot was £15,200.

Adding the fees and the cost of the plot to the building cost gives the total cost of the house – £47,000. It was valued when finished at £65,000, giving a saving of £18,000 by selfbuilding. That's lucrative enough for me!

(For comparison, average male earnings in 1987 were £11,400. Spon's Price Book for that year gives the hourly wage rate of a 'craft operative' as £4-60.)

If you wish to generalize from the figures, bear in mind these points:

I was very lucky obtaining the plot, probably about £5,000 below its market value.

The figures don't include the interest charged on the mortgage while building.

On the other hand, the actual cost was £3,050 (the hypothetical value of my labour) less than the figure above.

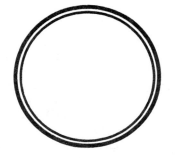

CHAPTER 11

A SIDEWAYS GLANCE AT A COMMERCIAL
BUILDER

WHILE I WAS BUILDING my house, a commercial builder – I'll call him
'Alex' – built a house on the adjacent plot. Naturally, I followed his
progress with interest. Here is an account of some of the points I noted.

Alex first approached me on April 1st 1987, asking about the adjacent
building plot. He told me he was going to put up a house in only two
months. Was that an April Fool's joke or a boast? A mere two weeks
later (he hadn't yet received Planning Permission), work started. The
first day, the site was stripped and pegged out. The following morning,
the trenches were dug. (The digger put a 'foot' through one of my
drains – Alex promised to repair it.) In the afternoon, the concrete was
poured. They were using the fast trench-fill method for the foundations, filling the trenches up almost to ground level. They received
three truckfuls of readymix, and had plenty of water added to make it,
in their words, "like pea soup". [As Rita Blooman mentioned in the
first chapter, adding water weakens concrete.] They established the
levels for the top of the concrete using an optical level. Somehow,
though, they missed out a step in a cross-wall trench, with the result
that its surface sloped from one end to the other.

The concrete was allowed to go off over Easter, and then the brickies
arrived. They had to contend with the sloping level. In parts they raised
the level with a course of pigs (bricks on their side), and in parts they
lowered it by slicing bricks along their length. And so they managed to
get the coursing level. It also turned out that the setting out was not very
accurate – the diagonals differed by 4″. But they carried on regardless.
Alex and the brickies had arranged to borrow my water supply, but on
the first day they also wanted to borrow a barrow, plasticizer, and petrol
– they didn't seem very professionally organized!

After a couple of days, the foundation walls had been finished, and
Alex filled the base with reject sand (sand with some stone in it). This is
half the price of stone, but it can hardly be approved of as hardcore. The

concrete slab was to be the finished floor, but they only managed to float its surface off once, and it was rather rough.

In the last week of April, the brickies started building up the external walls. Alex had chosen a rather costly facing brick, twice the price of mine. The cavities were filled with polystyrene slabs. Laying to the line, each brickie was laying about four bricks a minute. (Though pointing took a little extra time.)

In the first week of May, when some window frames were already in place, Alex told me that he had just received Planning consent. Did he sound a little relieved? He had reckoned that he was building a house that nobody could object to, and he'd sounded out all the neighbours beforehand. Nonetheless, he must have been taking some risk.

The pair of brickies made rapid progress, and a couple of weeks after starting from the dpc, the building was ready for joisting. And a week or so later, the brickies were putting on the wall plate.

When the roof trusses had been put on, the brickies returned to build up the gables. However, Alex, despite his promises, still hadn't repaired my drain. So I threatened to cut off his water supply, which would have brought work to a halt. The next day the drain was repaired.

By the end of May, the gables had been put up, and the roof tiled. The tilers, working without any supervision, made the flush verges rather too flush, and the result looked mean. Even Alex didn't seem pleased with it.

It took only one-and-a-half months to get the roof on from first stripping the site – good going. And only two months from first finding the plot, which must be some sort of record. (Don't try to emulate it!)

Straightaway, the plumber and the chippy moved in. The stairs were quickly fixed – a simple, straight flight – and the upper floor laid. Then the electrician started work. In the middle week of June, the plasterers boarded and skimmed upstairs. And the following week they plastered downstairs. By the end of June, the chippy had finished his second fix – or so he thought.

One day I noticed Alex's labourer digging a rather odd hole in the front garden. What was that for, I asked. The answer was that they'd covered over the water pipe before the Water Authority had inspected it. The Authority was now insisting on this hole being dug to check how deep the pipe had been laid. On a somewhat similar theme, I was told that Alex had informed the NHBC rather late about his building. So the NHBC hadn't been able to start inspecting it until some time after the foundations had been finished. For this, Alex was 'fined' £150.

Later on in the construction, the NHBC inspector took a very firm line over the bracing in the roof. The NHBC regulations had changed twice in a year, and Alex's chippy had become quite confused. He even came to me, asking how I'd done mine. Anyway, at the inspector's bidding, he had to change the bracing three times – not at all easy with the roof already tiled. He felt sick in his stomach about it, he said.

And the chippy's misfortunes were compounded by another mistake he'd made. One evening, a couple interested in buying the house came to look at it, and I showed them round. Whose interest should I support, my present neighbour Alex, or these possible future neighbours? – a little moral dilemma. Anyway, I pointed the chippy's mistake out to the couple. On the landing, there was supposed to be a hand-rail supported on studwork around the stairwell. But the chippy had mistakenly taken the studwork right up to ceiling. Instead of balustrades, he'd made walls. The following day, the couple agreed to buy the house – but the unwanted walls had to come down. So once again the chippy had to put in time and effort for no extra reward.

By the middle of July, the house was glazed, and the decorator had put the first coat of stain-paint on the external timber.

The work slowed down somewhat in the last six weeks, as plumber, chippy, electrician and decorator returned to finish off work, to make good defects, or to change things to the wishes of the incoming owners. There was also some activity in the garden, putting down paths, turf and the like. The house was more or less ready by the end of August when the new owners moved in. From time to time Alex and the tradesmen were called back to remedy defects. Eventually, the lady of the house lost patience and told Alex that she never wanted to see him again.

What about Alex's boast that he'd build a house in a couple of months? Well, he had the roof on in only a month and a half, which is perhaps what he meant. But overall, the house took four-and-a-half months to build, which is probably a typical time for commercial house building. You can see from the above account what a lot of mistakes were made. If as a selfbuilder you make mistakes, don't be downhearted – it happens in the trade too.

Nonetheless, financially Alex was doing well. He told me the finances of the house: £15K for the plot, £27K to build, £3K for fees, interest and the like. He sold it for £60K, giving a profit of £15K. In times previous, Alex used to drive around in a Rolls. Then his plant hire firm had "gone through a bad patch" and he'd lost much of his wealth. Now he was putting up eight houses a year, and it looked like he was heading back to Rolls status again.

Alex's all-in building cost of £27,000 was comparable to the cost for my house (see the previous chapter). Although his house was four-bedroomed, the floor area was a few square metres smaller than mine. The house was very simple and quick to build, with no complex parts.

"All I really want to build is a box", Alex once explained to me. "I'd rather have the throughput than a bit more on the price."

☆   ☆   ☆   ☆   ☆

Here is a quotation from *The Simple Home* written by an American poet, Charles Keeler, and published in 1904. It may be from another time and another place, but it still seems relevant in Britain nearly a century later. The extract is the start of the chapter *The Building of the House*:

> *Home making is one of the sacred tasks of life, for the home is the family temple, consecrated to the service of parents and offspring. As the strength of the state is founded upon family life, so is the strength of society based upon the home. The building of the home should be an event of profound importance. It should be with man as it is with birds, the culminating event after courtship and marriage, upon which all the loving thought and energy of the bridal pair is bestowed. How often in our modern American life do we find a far different procedure! The real estate agent and the investor confer, and as a result we have rows of houses put up to sell, to shiftless house seekers who are too indifferent to think out their needs, and helplessly take what has been built for the trade. The taint of commercialism is over these homes, and all too often the life within them is shallow and artificial.*

Strong words! Perhaps we would consider them excessive today, but there is at their heart a very valid sentiment.

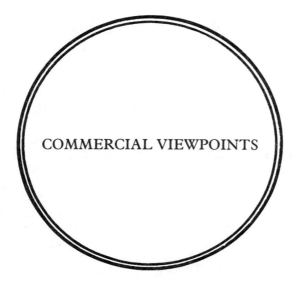

PART THREE

COMMERCIAL VIEWPOINTS

THIS LAST SECTION contains two interviews with people who are commercially involved with selfbuild. Both have been involved in their businesses for several years, so they have a good deal of experience to pass on. (Having said that, let me add that featuring them here is not an endorsement of their businesses. I have no direct experience of either firm.)

Individual selfbuilders often go for a house-building package, and the first interview is with the managing director of a company that supplies such packages.

On the other hand, some selfbuilders work in groups, and these groups are usually set up and guided by consultants. The second interview is with a managing director from the oldest and largest firm of selfbuild consultants.

CHAPTER 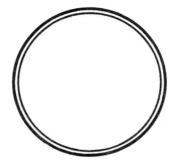 12

HOUSE-BUILDING PACKAGES

THERE ARE COMPANIES that offer house-building packages or kits – a house design with most of the building materials required to go with it. This must be an attractive proposition for many selfbuilders – all they've got to do is to put the stuff together! Moreover, as part of the total package, the companies usually undertake to obtain Planning Permission and Building Regulations approval. And they may also offer experienced advice, which can be most useful to the novice builder.

Most of the companies offering such packages are timber-frame manufacturers. But two companies specialize in traditional construction: Rationalised Building Services Ltd (RBS) in Cardiff, and Design and Materials Ltd (D & M) near Worksop. These companies have a lot of experience of selfbuilding, so I went to Cardiff to interview Derrick Anscombe, the managing director of RBS.

☆　　☆　　☆　　☆　　☆

Can you say first of all how this firm was started?

MR ANSCOMBE: It was started, not by me, but by other people connected with the building industry. In 1966 they conceived the idea of a building system as a package deal. One of them was Murray Armor [the author of 'Build Your Own Home']. The other person was a builder, and they got together with an architect and conceived a package deal for house building.

Was this aimed at selfbuilders or small builders?

MR ANSCOMBE: It was primarily aimed at the small builder. In fact when RBS started, all the dealings, even for individuals, were done through builders. But later, selfbuild came into its own.

So what services do you offer selfbuilders?

MR ANSCOMBE: To start with, we do all the planning for the ground works up to the working drawings, including surveys, drainage layouts, road layouts. What's required depends on the size of the development, whether it's a one-off plot or a multiple development – either for selfbuilders or builders. Our biggest selfbuild site was sixteen houses.

That was a group?

MR ANSCOMBE: Yes; we've had a few groups, mostly in the South East, though we've had groups in Wales as well.

How extensive is the package you supply?

MR ANSCOMBE: We start with foundation materials, and we supply the bulk of the construction materials through to the internal finishing materials, including bathroom suite. We exclude things like kitchens, plumbing and electrics.

It's a pretty comprehensive package.

How much choice does the customer have?

MR ANSCOMBE: He has a choice (depending on what the Local Authority specifies as well) regarding exterior materials; this can be facing bricks, blocks or stone. He has a choice of internal finishes – for example, the type of internal doors, type and colour of bathroom suite – from the range that we offer.

Say a customer didn't like your bathroom suites?

MR ANSCOMBE: Then we make them an allowance, and they are at liberty to buy elsewhere. This normally only happens with bathroom suites. We offer quite a comprehensive range, but there's always something else that somebody wants.

How much more do your materials cost compared to the discounted price a selfbuilder could get at builders' merchants?

MR ANSCOMBE: We like to think that they can do no better by going anywhere else. As a group, we buy all our materials at competitive prices, so we can pass these on to the trade and selfbuild people. And they too get the benefit of trade prices.

We don't doubt, for a moment, that the people we quote for a package go to a merchant's and price up against us. And when they come back to us, we know we must be competitive.

Speaking from my own experience, I didn't have the know-how as a novice selfbuilder to do that. So maybe not all your customers do price it up?

MR ANSCOMBE: At least 50% of our customers are builders. They come back to us time and time again. Some of them have been with us twenty years; I think this speaks for itself. We offer the same terms to the selfbuilder. We've done some very large developments. We did one in South Wales that was over 200. We're doing one in Aberystwyth, which is over 100 so far.

For your architectural services do you charge extra?

MR ANSCOMBE: Naturally, we build a small cost into the price of the package for the architectural services we include.

All the advice that we give is complimentary.

How readily available is that advice to the selfbuilder?

MR ANSCOMBE: It's available to anybody at any time.

Even after they've paid their money over to you?

MR ANSCOMBE: Oh, yes. Once they decide to use our services, we stick with them right through the construction and call on the site regularly.

How regular is 'regularly'?

MR ANSCOMBE: It all depends on how near or far the site is. If it's local, it's probably once a week. If it's far afield, like in Devon or Cornwall, every two or three weeks – more often if our assistance is requested.

We offer the service, and we're there to advise. If we see things we don't like, we tell them and ask for the mistakes to be corrected.

So then they can either follow your advice, or not?

MR ANSCOMBE: That's right. We hope they will.

People who are building their own sometimes need all the assistance they can get.

Calling on our customers, I see that the amount of homework they do, before they even start, is quite considerable. They buy several books on the subject. We wouldn't think much of anybody who didn't research the project first.

That's the way we feel we score; the technical advice and assistance we give is invaluable. Even builders say that our services are worth a lot to them. They can get on with the building, and they don't have to waste their time buying. If they buy a package from us, they've only got to get on the phone and say "Next stage, please".

Do you have a portfolio of designs?

MR ANSCOMBE: We have a standard catalogue which shows about 30 of our many designs, but we very rarely sell one of these nowadays. We seek to introduce ourselves through the brochure. Ninety-nine percent of people want an individual design, which we do for them. (It could be just a variation to a standard design.) Unless we're dealing with speculative builders, our customers are inclined to go away from the standard designs – they want something special.

How much will your design service be costing them then?

MR ANSCOMBE: The cost is a nominal sum and depends on the size and complexity of the design.

Do people ever ask for what you might call unusual designs?

MR ANSCOMBE: Yes. People ask for all sorts of designs. People have come a long way from the rectangulars and the squares; they like something a bit different. Until we advise them, they don't always realize the cost involved. There's nothing cheaper than a rectangular bungalow. When you start coming to hips and valleys and unusual shapes, it starts getting more expensive.

It's surprising how designs change. You get a run on some designs, and then the trends change, like fashion.

Do you know why?

MR ANSCOMBE: No. It just seems that you have fashion trends.

I must say that housing designs are getting far better, far more attractive, more individual.

In addition to producing the design, you also obtain the required Planning consents?

MR ANSCOMBE: Yes. If they haven't got any Planning Permission when clients come to us, they can either go for Full Planning, which is a gamble – whether they get it or not – or they can just go for Outline Planning Permission.

If the plot already has Outline Permission, it's just a matter of getting the details sorted out and approved. We might have to change the design halfway through because it's not exactly what the planners require – it could be too big, too small, the wrong shape, *et cetera*. It's all part of our package to get it right in the end, to suit the client and the planners.

Would you advise somebody to go for Outline Planning Permission first, rather than Full Planning Permission?

MR ANSCOMBE: Again, it depends of the site. If it's out in the country or on the edge of a village or badly situated, then we do advise that perhaps they go for Outline first, and so avoid any cost of detailed plans.

In case it's turned down?

MR ANSCOMBE: That's right. All you've got to do for Outline Permission is to submit a site plan, and there's really no cost involved.

Where it is an infill plot in the middle of a town, and there shouldn't be any reason for refusing an application, then we suggest that they take the gamble and go for Full Planning Permission.

We always recommend that, before they do anything, they go and have a chat with the Planning officer. If he seems doubtful, then we say "Right, go for Outline then". If he says "No problem" – we could still get problems! But it is for the client to decide what application we make on his behalf.

What would you advise people to do if their Planning application were turned down? Is it worth appealing?

MR ANSCOMBE: We look at the pros and cons. If we feel it's worth it, then we'll do the appeal for them. If it's a hopeless looking case, then we'll advise them not to or to go to an appeal consultant. There are firms who specialize in Planning appeals.

But if it looks hopeful, we will do it with them. We attend meetings and submit the appeal to the Department of the Environment or the Welsh Office.

How long does the whole process take?

MR ANSCOMBE: Anything up to twelve months. You have to appeal within six months of a refusal, and then it takes from 6 to 12 months before you receive a decision.

Do you charge extra for making an appeal?

MR ANSCOMBE: No. All we've got to do is to fill in some forms. We've got everything else – the documents, the drawings, *et cetera* – that you have to submit with an application. We do expect the customer to participate and prepare a statement giving his reasons for appealing.

The Building Regulations approval is more straightforward?

MR ANSCOMBE: That's in our own architect's hands. Sometimes there's something required in the way of additional information – detail which is easily supplied. With Building Regulations, you've only got to comply with what the Local Authority require.

And you deal with that?

MR ANSCOMBE: Oh, yes; that's part of our service. We undertake to get these things through.

Do you find the building inspectors vary a lot?

MR ANSCOMBE: We get building inspectors who are far stricter than others, but our customers are advised that this is for their benefit.

There's no point in putting their backs up, either by jumping the gun and going ahead of them – I'm talking about the people working on site – or perhaps going against their advice, or actually telling the building inspector what his job is. It's the wrong thing to put the inspector's back up because you need his help anyway. A building inspector can be a lot of help to a person on site.

The building inspector obviously knows more about the Building Regulations than anybody else does. You might not agree with what he says, but if that's the Regulation, that's the way it has to be done.

How do most selfbuilders get on about getting an architects' certificate?

MR ANSCOMBE: We can arrange that with our consultant architects; they're all qualified architects. They make four or five visits during construction, criticize where necessary, and certify if the job is to their satisfaction.

That's an extra cost?

MR ANSCOMBE: It's an extra cost; yes. It depends on how far away the site is and the number of visits required. But the average cost is about £350, or more.

How many stages do you make the deliveries in?

MR ANSCOMBE: A lot of materials go direct from works – blocks, bricks and things like that – and they're phased in as they're wanted. Our ex-stock deliveries we try to keep to three. Once upon a time, it was two, but now, due to the volume of materials we send, it is three. It can be as many as half a dozen.

How many brick companies do you deal with?

MR ANSCOMBE: All of them. There's a wide choice of bricks; it all depends on the area and the Local Authority requirements.

Do you include tiling as well?

MR ANSCOMBE: We actually do the tiling. We've got teams of subcontractors who do the tiling for us. That's all part of the package.

Does it include the glazing?

MR ANSCOMBE: Yes; double glazing – sealed units.

Do you have much trouble with sealed units?

MR ANSCOMBE: Nowadays, relatively few. In the early days of sealed units, you used to get quite a lot break down.

Do many customers ask for traditional timber roofs, or is it all roof trusses?

MR ANSCOMBE: Most of them are truss roofs. But we do supply a cut roof if people eventually want to turn it into another room upstairs or if the design is a dormer.

You have to be quite skilled to cut the timbers for a traditional roof. Do you supply the timbers already cut?

MR ANSCOMBE: No; we normally supply them to the nearest lengths, to be cut on site.

You supply the plasterboard?

MR ANSCOMBE: Yes.

Most selfbuilders find traditional plastering quite difficult. Do you think they are better going for dry lining?

MR ANSCOMBE: A lot of houses are studded upstairs [and dry lined]. Some people now opt to have studded walls throughout if it is practical. (Though in houses you probably have to have one or two load-bearing walls in traditional blockwork.) They prefer to dry line. And then they can use a finish that you roll on; you get an effect of skimming. You put it on with a roller.

It's fairly easy to do?

MR ANSCOMBE: You need a little bit of practice. I've done it.

It's easier than traditional plastering?

MR ANSCOMBE: I don't think that anyone but a professional can do plastering properly.

Are all your packages for brick-and-block construction, or are some timber-frame?

MR ANSCOMBE: We do mostly traditional, but we also get orders for timber-frame.

What are the pros and cons of the two methods?

MR ANSCOMBE: None whatsoever. It's just a question of the customer's choice, as far as we're concerned. There's little to choose between them, price-wise or value for money.

So you wouldn't recommend the customer to choose one or the other?

MR ANSCOMBE: No; we can offer both.

The material content is more expensive with a timber-frame package, but it's swings and roundabouts, and you save on labour.

How much more expensive is the materials cost?

MR ANSCOMBE: 25% to 30% over the whole RBS package.

You said timber-frame needs less labour. Can you say how much faster it is?

MR ANSCOMBE: You're talking about dispensing with a lot of the wet trades. When the timber-frame house arrives on site, it's just a case of constructing it – two to three days, depending on the size and complexity.

So within a week you've got a roof on?

MR ANSCOMBE: That's possible. You can get it tiled immediately, and then you've got a covered area to work in. You take the brickwork up the outside afterwards, and you can be working inside at the same time.

With traditional, of course, you've got to build up all the external walls before you can get it roofed and start on the inside. It takes a bit longer. We've had two bungalows built in a week in traditional, but they were special cases.

It would take a selfbuilder who was an amateur bricklayer quite a lot longer than that, wouldn't it?

MR ANSCOMBE: Yes.

They work pretty hard in selfbuild groups. They are normally set about 23 hours a week on average. Everybody in the group works for that 23 hours, and more. But they've got to do a minimum.

I think that most of our developments usually take 3 to 6 months to complete each house.

That's in a group?

MR ANSCOMBE: Yes.

What about individuals? How long do they take?

MR ANSCOMBE: About four to six months; some go over a year. It depends on how much time they like to put into it themselves.

How much of the work do most people do themselves?

MR ANSCOMBE: I should think that most people subcontract out the difficult work. They put out things like brick or block laying. Plastering they would put out if it was traditional. They tackle most of the rest themselves. You get some people who do the lot themselves, but you'll find that most of them will subcontract a certain part of it.

You'll also find that some women get very involved with selfbuild, and they're pretty good at it too.

It's usually a husband and wife, isn't it?

MR ANSCOMBE: Yes. The husband's out at work while the build is going on, so the wife helps organize the subcontractors, *et cetera*.

You've got to debate whether it's worth doing it all yourself, or subcontract some trades.

It takes a long time if you do it yourself.

MR ANSCOMBE: That's right. Perhaps for a few hundred pounds you can get all the blockwork done, and it brings you forward that much quicker.

I've got one going at the moment. He built his first one himself, and he said "Never again". But I notice he's doing it all himself, again.

That raises the question of how soon after the first one you can build another. If you sell a house, you don't pay any capital gains tax on it if it has been your home.

MR ANSCOMBE: Yes, but if you did it too often, they'd start asking questions. You've got to live in it for a minimum of twelve months, otherwise you become liable to capital gains tax.

We've got one customer who selfbuilt four times, and now he's a builder and still coming to RBS.

How much money do you reckon you can save by doing a selfbuild?

Mr Anscombe: We quote figures of anything up to 40% on the cost of construction. That's based on information supplied by customers.

Without the land?

Mr Anscombe: That's right. Land prices can vary from £15,000 to £250,000.

Are you able to help selfbuilders find land at all? D & M say they do that.

Mr Anscombe: We know quite a few estate agents, and we do ask them to give us support. People do ask us if we can help find land, and we will advise them how to go about it.

Do you find Local Authorities helpful in that respect?

Mr Anscombe: Some. Some Local Authorities are pretty good at offering land for individual development. In fact, if people do ask us about land, we suggest they approach the Local Authorities – they sometimes release land for private build.

You said you dealt with group selfbuilds. Were they run by selfbuild consultants?

Mr Anscombe: No; not the selfbuild groups that we have supplied. We have more or less been their consultants as well.

How were the groups formed? Did you set them up?

Mr Anscombe: No. A group of people come to us and say "We want to build our own". And we advise them as much as we can, do all their Planning, and supply the packages.

The groups that we have dealt with didn't want to pay for a consultant. They felt that they could manage themselves with our assistance. We can offer a substantial amount of assistance that would probably be offered by the consultants anyway.

Do you know how these groups come into being?

Mr Anscombe: I think you get one or two individuals who get the idea of building their own, read up on it, and then advertise locally or ask friends to join them. Some of our clients in the Sussex area are employed in Gatwick Airport.

What do you think most selfbuilders find the most difficult part?

MR ANSCOMBE: It can be a pretty traumatic experience building your own home. Although once they've actually done it, a lot of people find it wasn't as traumatic as they'd expected. A good many of our customers do it again and again.

There's no area that comes to mind where selfbuilders tend to make mistakes?

MR ANSCOMBE: We find that selfbuilders do a very good job. They're probably looking for a little more perfection than the ordinary developer. I'm not saying that the developers don't do a good job, but we find that the selfbuilder is more fussy. Some of them really do turn out a nice house.

You hear occasionally of storms blowing down half-built walls, and things like that. In that case, the builder would need some more bricks and blocks. They'd have to pay extra for that?

MR ANSCOMBE: Oh, yes – an act of God, not RBS.

Have you known many accidents like that?

MR ANSCOMBE: No. You sometimes get damage during construction, for example to the joinery, and we have to supply replacements. They're advised to insure.

We have had one instance where a plumber set light to a roof and burnt a bungalow down.

And was it insured?

MR ANSCOMBE: No; neither our customer nor the plumber were insured.

We did quite well out of that. We supplied the pack all over again!

Have you any comments you'd like to make about anything?

MR ANSCOMBE: There's a lot of selfbuilders that I'd like to get in contact with, but the only difficulty is finding them. A lot of people form groups throughout the country, and we're sure we can be of considerable assistance if we could only find out where they are and who they are.

It is hard to get in contact with selfbuilders. There's no channel for them, is there?

MR ANSCOMBE: There used to be. There used to be the Selfbuild Association based in Wiltshire, but it folded through lack of support.

We thought it could have been a good thing for the selfbuilder. The chap who ran it had himself been a selfbuilder, and there was a Government trustee involved. It had Government support at the time.

Do you advertise?

MR ANSCOMBE: In the *Daily Mail Book of Plans*. We get a good response from that. We do local advertising mostly. We advertise in South Wales and the West Country, and other parts of the country.

So although you cover the UK, most of your business is in the West?

MR ANSCOMBE: We do a lot in Wales because we're located in Wales. We used to have an office in Yorkshire, which brought us a lot of business in the North – we started in Yorkshire.

How did the firm come to be transferred down here?

MR ANSCOMBE: The marketing policy in 1969 was to form marketing companies with builders' merchants throughout the country. They formed one in South Wales which was called Pauls-RBS Ltd. Eventually, Pauls-RBS grew bigger than RBS. Pauls were owned by the British Dredging group of companies at that time, and they bought out RBS and brought it down here. Four years ago, we joined the Prestoplan Homes group.

How did you personally get involved with it?

MR ANSCOMBE: I happened to be with the builders' merchants, Pauls, that RBS teamed up with. When the company was formed, I was offered the job of running it and took it from there.

So RBS, D & M, and Prestoplan are now all in the same group. Are you marketing Prestoplan's timber-frames?

MR ANSCOMBE: Indirectly. They manufacture for us, for our designs. We're autonomous as far as design is concerned.

For marketing purposes, you don't divide the country up with D & M?

MR ANSCOMBE: No. As far as we're concerned, we compete with them – in a friendly way, of course. We may both go after the same job. One of us will be disappointed if the other gets the order.

Are there any other companies in your line of business?

MR ANSCOMBE: I should think Prestoplan are probably the biggest suppliers of timber-frame packages. There are several others – Bristol Timber Frame are one firm known to us in this area.

There are also the Scandinavian companies that offer timber-frame packages.

MR ANSCOMBE: I don't know how they sell in the UK: they're expensive. Mind you, the specification is fantastic. The quality of the materials – probably the timber's twice as big as ours, the windows are thicker than ours (triple glazing and things like that). And the roof structures, I think, are built to take a hurricane.

There's a lot of timber-frame manufacturers. But as far as doing a package in traditional materials, the only two I know of that do that is ourselves and D & M.

And they were both started by Murray Armor?

MR ANSCOMBE: Yes – in partnership with others, of course.

D & M have their joinery made to their own designs, but you don't?

MR ANSCOMBE: No. We used to in the early days, but because of the volumes of stock required, we decided to move over to standard joinery. Purpose made joinery is a lot more expensive.

Who are the people who go out and do the site visiting? What are their qualifications?

MR ANSCOMBE: Pure building knowledge and experience. They've been in the building industry in various capacities for a long time. I have done quantity surveying and know quite a lot about building construction.

What I have found was that from books you could read up what was the normal thing, but when anything became a little bit abnormal, a bit strange, then you didn't have the knowledge to deal with it.

MR ANSCOMBE: There's a lot of trial-and-error and practical experience needed. We get people saying 'So and so doesn't fit', and it's so obvious that they can make it fit if they apply common sense and logic.

Have you any thoughts about metrication?

MR ANSCOMBE: It would be alright if it was completely standardized. But you still get imperial and you still get metric, in materials and design. Materials are the worst – either metric or imperial or a combination of both!

I think, if you're of the old school like myself, you still think imperial and convert all the time. For example, we do a metric design and say it's 1,400 square feet.

To me, it's all a mess.

MR ANSCOMBE: Yes; I don't think they've got it quite right yet. I don't think there's been any changes for a few years now; they got to a certain stage and it's remained there.

Have you built your own house?

MR ANSCOMBE: Yes; with a RBS package!

How long did yours take?

MR ANSCOMBE: About three years so far. *Laughter.*

It's finished except for external decoration. It's been ready like that for the last twelve months. We're living in it. I suppose to get it habitable it took us about six months – my son working full-time on it, me working weekends and nights. We built timber-frame.

How much of the work did you do yourselves?

MR ANSCOMBE: Most of it. The only thing that we subcontracted was the external blockwork and external render. Otherwise, we did everything ourselves.

One last question: do you think that selfbuild will become more widespread?

MR ANSCOMBE: I think it's a question of land availability. I think that, if people could get land at a reasonable price, they would go into it in a far bigger way, and many more would build their own homes.

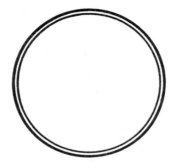

CHAPTER 13

SELFBUILD CONSULTANTS

SOME SELFBUILD is done in groups, in which a number of people co-operate together to build houses for themselves. This makes sense in a number of respects:

Often the groups contain a number of building tradesmen, so a good deal of skill is available; buying in bulk can bring substantial quantity discounts; responsibilities can be shared; and there is often comradeship.

A few of these groups are formed by would-be selfbuilders coming together themselves. But most are set up by selfbuild consultants. Since selfbuild is their business, these consultants must know a lot about the subject. So I went along for an interview with Diane Dring, who manages the central region of Homesmith Consultants.

☆　　☆　　☆　　☆　　☆

Can you tell me a little of the history of Homesmith?

MISS DRING: The company was formerly the Wadsworth Group. At the end of 1988, we changed our name to Homesmith – 'smith' like 'blacksmith' – specialists in providing the necessaries for people to actually build homes.

The Wadsworth Group first started about 22 years ago, initially in Yorkshire – helping groups of people to get together to build homes for themselves, using Housing Corporation funding at the time with land chiefly acquired from Local Authorities. These had a particular interest in assisting people into owner occupation.

And it was started by Colin Wadsworth?

MISS DRING: Correct.

Why did he do it?

MISS DRING: He actually took part in a scheme himself. It lasted three years, and he took over most of the officers' roles. He became chairman, secretary, treasurer – a leading light from amongst the membership.

So already there were people setting up schemes?

MISS DRING: No; not organizing them. At the time, there was no professional management. The Government had directed the Housing Corporation to tell people how to do it, but at the time, there was no formal professional management. He took part in this scheme which took three years.

Once he'd completed the scheme, he found himself receiving numerous enquiries from similar-minded people – "How do we go about it?". At the time he was working for the National Savings Bank. So he started advising free of charge, on a part-time interest basis really. This gathered momentum, and he found himself in the position of making a decision – whether to leave the bank with its full-time security and branch out into selfbuild management, or to stop giving out advice. He obviously chose the former.

Quite a bold decision?

MISS DRING: Absolutely, at the time – we're talking twenty-odd years ago. So he started in a very small way in Yorkshire, which was where he was based. His scheme was based at Sowerby Bridge. He then, within a couple of years, had taken in two part-time partners, one based in Blackpool and a further one in Yorkshire. Again, people had contacted him and said they were interested in the subject, and the business just really started from there.

I joined the company in 1976. At that time we had an office in Brigg (South Humberside), Blackpool, Huddersfield and one in Bristol. I was based at the Brigg office.

What was your background?

MISS DRING: Hotel management – nothing at all to do with housing.

But our work is about people. Selfbuild is a way of life; it's not just work. It's involved with people's aims, hopes, ambitions, frustrations; and there's a strong family aspect to it.

How did you come to be involved?

MISS DRING: I was a relief manager of a hotel for the group I was working for at the time. I decided I needed a change of direction – being single, I couldn't move on to managing a hotel permanently. The company policy was that it had to be a couple.

So I retreated to my parents at Scunthorpe, and I was quite bored after working in the hotel industry where you work very long hours. A girl-friend suggested I went to Manpower, who had just started a temporary staff agency. My first job was four days at Wadsworth and Simpson. And basically, I didn't leave.

By the following New Year, I found myself based at Petersfield in Hampshire, opening up a new region. We commenced schemes in Eastbourne, Lewes, Newhaven – that sort of area. The office is now based in Lewes in Sussex. They're currently building about 350 houses a year.

In '79, I moved up to the Midlands to open a regional office here [in Atherstone, Warwickshire]. So this is our tenth year. We now have a field office at Baldock in Hertfordshire.

How many houses were you responsible for last year – or is that a commercial secret?

MISS DRING: No; not at all. Last year, we built 220 from this region. With all four regions it was about 650. This year (1989), we anticipate about 1,200.

Murray Armour estimates in his book that about 2,000 houses a year are built in groups. Do you think that's about right?

MISS DRING: Yes; I do.

Selfbuild looks as though it's about to really take off, don't you think?

MISS DRING: Yes; we've seen every sign of that. It's not too long ago I remember sitting at board meetings saying "Well, if we build 37 houses per region, we'll break even as a company".

So now you're making lots of money are you?

MISS DRING: We're working very hard, I would like to add. And I think that you can appreciate selfbuild is twenty-four hours a day, seven days a week. We run an office here to back up the schemes. We have twenty-two sites building at the moment. And we do all the accounting, all the administration work, together with the ordering of materials where necessary.

Twenty-two sites in your region?

MISS DRING: Yes; just in my region.

You can imagine the administration involved behind that. And then of course the lads are building on site at weekends and in their spare time, so we have to be available then as well.

Are you the largest of the selfbuild consultants?

MISS DRING: Yes; we've been going longer. We're the biggest in terms of output. My selfbuilders say we're the best.

But they wouldn't know any differently, would they?

MISS DRING: Some of them do. Some of them have done schemes with other consultants before.

In what respects are you the best?

MISS DRING: We're the most organized. We provide the widest range of services to the selfbuilder in terms of information, presentation, organization, systems procedures, and discipline – which is a vital factor in selfbuild. When you've got a bunch of people, all with equal say, there has to be discipline, a very strong discipline, established from day one. Once the group comes together as a unit, they can relax and make allowances because they know everybody's level of commitment and responsibilities. But initially, it must be quite defined: you do this and that happens to you. And they love it. The harder it is the more they love it.

So you supply this discipline from outside?

MISS DRING: Yes; we have six meetings before we commence work on site. We go through every aspect of the scheme.

Do you sometimes have groups which revolt against you?

MISS DRING: We have groups that don't take our advice.

What happens to them?

MISS DRING: Nothing; we work with them. If that's their decision, that's their decision. We're still there. And eventually, when they realize that they've made the wrong one, then we say "Right, let's go forward". We work together as a team. We've got to learn, as well as the selfbuilders. The selfbuilders employ us. The association employs us to act as their managers. Now if they choose not to take our advice, that's up to them. We will minute it, and we will explain why we're recommending a certain course of action, but if they wish to take some other course, that is their entitlement.

What is the basis on which you're paid?

MISS DRING: It is per site. There is a fee agreed for the development of the site, and stage payments agreed; and we have a mutual exchange of contracts.

And you say when you're setting the scheme up what that payment will be?

Miss Dring: Yes; it's all laid out. Each member has a full, detailed bill of costings, which takes him through the normal build: rates, materials, items to the general overheads, land purchase, insurances, Planning Permission, roads and sewer costs – all this sort of thing. And there is a section which includes professional fees, which shows how much they are going to pay the solicitor, the architect, ourselves, the surveyors, the structural engineers – and the timing of the payments. So it's all quite open.

What do your fees come to then?

Miss Dring: Generally 7½% of the market value of the site (the projected market value on commencement of the scheme, without inflation). So that it is fixed even if the market does go up over the course of the scheme.

Are you sometimes responsible for putting the roads in?

Miss Dring: No. We have no relationship at all with suppliers, road contractors or anything like that. Sometimes the group can construct the road, under our supervision. Or if the road is a fairly large and complex one, then it will be contracted out. We would put it out to tender.

And the road would be put in before building starts?

Miss Dring: Often we'd be doing the two simultaneously, sometimes to the road contractor's dismay. But time is money. We can't afford to sit back two months with interest clocking up without development.

How do you go about setting a scheme going? Do you look for the land first?

Miss Dring: Yes; that's the first ingredient. We've got to have suitable land, and to have bought it at a price which will show a good saving to the group selfbuild. In general, we're looking for 25% savings.

And you get those plots by buying a lot of plots together?

Miss Dring: Yes.
  If I talk from the beginning:
  Basically, our land acquisitions come from a variety of sources. We're offered an awful lot of land from developers. They like to have us next door to them. We make good bed partners; we're not in

competition. A small part of our land bank comes from Local Authorities, and a small part has been bought on the open market (either by tender or private treaty). And then we buy quite a lot of land from private people (farmers and local land-owners), who have seen selfbuild somewhere around and think it's an excellent idea for local people.

And they come to you, do they?

MISS DRING: Very much so. We're more reactive than active in searching out land.

A very nice situation to be in.

MISS DRING: Yes; it is.

We've built up over the years a reputation for good quality housing. The sites are run very professionally, similar to a developer. They're kept tidy; the work is in an orderly fashion; we don't leave materials lying all over the place.

So once we've been offered a piece of land, we would then carry out a viability study on the site. We would look at the surrounding area, decide what sort of house types ought to go onto the site, and obtain from the local estate agents an approximate market value for them. We would then come back here and actually cost out the scheme to develop with those house types, taking into account ground conditions, infrastructure, the whole lot. We actually utilize a computer program which will then churn out the required land purchase price if we wish to save 25%, 20% or whatever. Then we go to final negotiations and agree a price.

We would then promote the scheme to the general public by means of an exhibition. We have videos, exhibition stands.

You advertise in the local paper?

MISS DRING: That's right; or on the radio, posters, that sort of thing.

Members of the public are invited to come in without obligation, usually between four o'clock and eight o'clock. They have a look at the general information on selfbuild, and collect a package about the actual project which shows the house types, projected costs on completion, current day values, location of the site, and, in general, full information about the site. They have an application form, which they're invited to complete and return to us within a period of time.

How many people show an interest at this stage?

MISS DRING: We expect 10% of the people who come to an exhibition to be of serious intent. We would expect 6% or 7% to actually apply –

the numbers come down very much. And from that, we fill our schemes.

As an example, we had an exhibition at Solihull recently. We had nearly two thousand people through the door. For 67 places, we've had over 300 applicants. Out of that, probably about 100 are suitable in terms of affordability, availability, all that sort of thing.

So you vet the people applying?

Miss Dring: Very much.

We go through the forms initially along the lines:

Affordability for the house type we've selected.

Availability to work at weekends.

What sort of skills they could offer the association.

We then, having short-listed, go to a personal interview stage with the member and his family. It's very important that the commitment from the family is with him. We're looking at their character, commitment, and intent – what do they actually want out of the scheme? Is it to move up the ladder? Do they want a better home with an equal mortgage? – all those sorts of reasons. We're looking for a balanced team of ages, characters, trades and DIY. We believe that selfbuild isn't just for skilled tradesmen, that the average chap, who's handy at home, enthusiastic, fit, and healthy, can put a lot into the scheme.

What's the usual ratio of tradesmen overall?

Miss Dring: Between 75% and 80% trades, 20% and 25% DIY. So we would have a labourer who's working with a bricklayer, a labourer who's working with the ground workers, the carpenters, the plumbers.

What about someone who wasn't a trades-person, nor DIY? They'd get rejected, would they?

Miss Dring: No, no, no; not necessarily. When I say 'DIY', we're talking in the main of someone who has built a patio at home, somebody who's keen – otherwise he wouldn't contemplate a selfbuild; he's not afraid of physical exertion. We've got teachers, accountants, policemen . . .

So having gone through the interview, we select the final team. We would then confirm their acceptance for a particular house type. Plots are actually drawn by ballot. A member is accepted for the house type, but he won't know where that is on the site until the second meeting of the whole group.

Are the house types usually all the same?

MISS DRING: No; we have a variety. We have a stable, shall we say, of different types.

We're very interested in estate layout. It's very important that the whole site is balanced, so our house types blend with each other. It's almost like a family, from two-bedrooms to four-bedrooms.

How does fairness come into this? People are putting equal amounts of labour in, yet at the end of the scheme they're going to get out smaller or bigger houses, aren't they?

MISS DRING: Correct.

People don't mind that?

MISS DRING: Not at all.

What we actually say is that you will all save the same percentage. Now the percentage of a two-bedroomed terrace in money terms will obviously be smaller than a detached four-bed, but it's equal effort. Each house type needs the other to make the scheme balance, and all the members need each other to actually carry out the work.

No; we don't have any problem with that at all.

We don't believe in creating, if we can at all help it, an estate of just four-bedroomed, detached houses. We believe in mixing people from different backgrounds.

How many houses do you have on an estate?

MISS DRING: It varies considerably. Probably the average is between 20 and 25. Our smallest scheme is 7, our largest is 44 in one group. We have in Luton two sites; one is for 68 units, which is two groups; another one is 78 units, which is three groups. So we split them to manageable sizes, but they're building simultaneously.

Do you find then that there's an optimum number of people in a group to interact together?

MISS DRING: Yes. I would say between 15 and 20 is a good number. It allows for an inclusion of all the trades and some general labour. In a small group of seven you'll be very lucky to include all the trades.

Even if they're not doing all the work, at least they'll be able to judge the subcontracted work.

What happens if you have too many people in a group? Why did you split the group of 78 units?

MISS DRING: We felt that was too large for the members to interact with each other. Seventy-eight people would not provide a community spirit. They wouldn't know half the people on the scheme. So we split it into three groups. The road pattern actually delineated just how we were going to split it.

The members and the families do actually get to know each other.

Do the members' wives work?

MISS DRING: It varies considerably from scheme to scheme. We've got schemes where the ladies actually do fulfil a practical aspect, and they've organized a *crèche*. The biggest problem is obviously small children. They've organized a *crèche* so half a dozen of them can be available and report to the site foreman for general work. Now that may vary from cleaning houses out after the plasterer's finished, to painting and decorating. Usually they're not involved in too much heavy physical work.

We had a group where we had difficult ground conditions, and they were putting in steel cages for the foundations. The ladies actually did all the tying of the steel. They said it was like weaving!

It varies considerably. On other schemes, the ladies pretty much take over the officers' roles. In the background, they're the secretary, treasurer. And then, just on a domestic front really, they'll organize lunch at weekends, even if it's just collecting fish and chips for the whole site and brewing up tea. It varies considerably.

Hasn't there been in the past a bit of male chauvenism about it? In the Seventies, weren't the rules of Colin Wadsworth that no women were allowed on site?

MISS DRING: Times have changed. Selfbuild has changed.

Are the people always married couples?

MISS DRING: No, no, no – often unmarried couples.

Single people?

MISS DRING: Sometimes; yes. Quite a variety. We do particularly encourage this. In some cases, we have two male partners.

Do you ever have any single women?

MISS DRING: We've not had any; no.

I have an ambition to organize a female selfbuild.

We do have a site where we have a subcontract bricklaying team and it's man, wife and son. The wife is the hod carrier and she knocks up the compo.

For somebody building their own house, what are the advantages of being in a group scheme?

MISS DRING: There are two sides to it really, one is a mental and one is a practical.

On the practical side, there is absolutely no need for someone to move into a caravan and live on site and, shall we say, rough it until the house is ready. In the main, people have to withdraw their equity to go ahead with an individual selfbuild. Within group selfbuild, this isn't a problem. They remain in their own houses until their new one's ready and they move in. So there's less hassle to the family.

A person needs very little money to join a scheme?

MISS DRING: We're now requiring £750 for loanstock, which is refunded at the end of the scheme.

On the mental level, I think it provides individuals with the confidence and security of working within a team. To the average person contemplating an individual selfbuild, all the responsibilities fall on him and his family; whereas in a group, they are spread out.

I imagine that sometimes there is some aggro in groups?

MISS DRING: Different groups have different problems, but yes, there are problems there.

I think you've got to appreciate that, with a group selfbuild, there's quite a lot of pressure attached to the hours that have to be put in. I mean, a chap's doing his normal job Monday to Friday; he's got to be on site early Saturday, early Sunday. At the same time, he's got to try and keep his family going and spend whatever time he can with them. So there may well be pressure at home. He's got to do certain things external to working on site. He's got to select his bathroom suite, his kitchen units – we allow him to have a choice of those. So when things go wrong on site – which they inevitably do in the building industry, nothing is straightforward – they react fairly diversely. A very placid man may suddenly react at the slightest problem; he may be sharp with one of his colleagues. We have almost a stress-relieving session once a month: We have a formal monthly meeting at which time members are encouraged to get everything off their chest, so that when they're back on site at the weekend they're working together quite amiably.

Is one of your representatives at that meeting?

MISS DRING: Yes; several. We have a site manager, a contracts manager, and then possibly, a representative from the accounts department – depending on what's on the agenda.

We try to encourage them, while they're on site, to utilize their time productively and to bring problems of that nature to the meeting – let's discuss it openly, democratically, and make a decision accordingly.

How do you make decisions – by voting?

Miss Dring: Yes; that's right. It's majority rule, two-thirds majority.

How long does it take from when you first advertise in an area until people get on site and start building?

Miss Dring: The average is three months.

Is that all?

Miss Dring: Yes; it's quick. It needs to be in the market for land. When a developer offers us a piece of land, he'll do that for a variety of reasons. But when it comes to a price, he usually wants it for next week. So we often enter into an early exchange of contracts, with a completion deferred until we've secured the detailed Planning Permission and set up a group. So – on average, about three months to get started. I think you have to harness people's enthusiasm as well. In the early days, when I started doing selfbuild, it would take twelve months for a scheme to start. That was hard work, maintaining interest.

Some people drop out, don't they?

Miss Dring: Oh, yes. The worst time is actually just after commencement on site. After spending three months talking about it and thinking about it, they have to actually get up every morning at seven at weekends. And perhaps their partner hadn't really envisaged the problems she would experience – no help with the kids, no help with shopping, no going out, no social life.

What happens when somebody wants to drop out?

Miss Dring: We would then take in a late-joining member. We usually maintain a reserve list. We would look: If we are losing a bricklayer, do we need another bricklayer? If we've got nobody suitable, we have to advertise.

Is the loanstock repaid to the people pulling out?

Miss Dring: They receive that back. But they lose the time they've put in; they get no recompense for that.

Do people ever get half way through a scheme and drop out?

Miss Dring: Yes; usually for reasons like job transferral and family circumstances.

So they lose all their hours, and the person coming in gains them?

Miss Dring: Yes; it's a little bit unfortunate, but as long as the association doesn't suffer – that's the important thing.

How long does a project usually last?

Miss Dring: The average is about 15 or 16 months. We have some groups that finish in 12 months, some that take 18 months. It depends upon how productive the group are in working as a team.

What proportion of the work is usually subcontracted?

Miss Dring: I haven't actually got a percentage figure that I can give you there, but we build in to the initial costings £2,000 per unit for subcontract labour. Depending on the skills that emerge from within the group, that is used, or maybe exceeded, or maybe under-used. In the main, it's for bricklaying and plastering.

What do you think is the value of the members' own labour?

Miss Dring: When we look at the scheme initially, we're looking for a minimum of 25% cost saving, which is current day values less projected scheme costs. By the time they've actually completed, in a normal year we're probably talking about savings of 35% to 40% because the market has moved on in terms of house values. I've analysed the 35% to 40%: there's a builder's profit (which a normal developer would build in), which would probably be 15% to 18% if you take off the marketing costs. So their labour is probably about 20% to 25%.

It sounds a very good deal.

Miss Dring: It is, if you're prepared to commit yourself. I personally believe that it's a very short length of time in life. If you actually devote yourself for 16 or 18 months, head down, forget about all the things that you normally do (fishing, football, that sort of thing) – at the end of it, you've got a tremendous product for just 18 months of your life.

You haven't done it?

Miss Dring: No! *Laughter.*
Most of my male staff have.

Is that how they come to you in the first place?

Miss Dring: Yes. I've seen them on schemes, recognized their capabilities, and then offered them a position after the job is finished.

You were telling me the advantages of being in a group scheme. What are the disadvantages?

Miss Dring: Having to work under a democratic rule, having to swallow and bite your tongue when you feel a decision is being made that is wrong. But as we explain, selfbuilders have a remarkable opportunity of doing a U-turn. They can make a decision because they are the builders and the purchasers. They can make a decision; try it out for three or four weeks; and if it's not right, they can come back again and rethink it through with the benefit of experience, and change direction. But some people find that very hard.

So it's working in a team with a democratic structure. And working in a team is sometimes difficult.

Most people, prior to joining a selfbuild scheme, only make decisions about holidays, which school the kids will go to, do we need a new pair of shoes, do we need to decorate. All of a sudden, they have to think collectively – what is good for the association? Then they will benefit if the association is successful. That's a hard pill to swallow at times.

So I see those as the disadvantages. Compared to individual selfbuild, the program is a lot longer – an individual selfbuild can probably be completed in nine to twelve months. Whereas a group selfbuild is three or four months longer. Sometimes that little addition can cause a bit of havoc, particularly if they've got to work through two winters. Wherever possible, we try to start them in the spring or early summer, so they get a good run up to winter, with internal work for the bad conditions. But it doesn't always work. We've had groups start between Christmas and New Year.

Does everybody have to put in a certain number of hours?

Miss Dring: Yes; there's a minimum number of hours a week.

What happens to the slackers then?

Miss Dring: Well, there's two reasons why someone won't have put their hours in. One is perhaps they're sick. Perhaps they've got a genuine, *bona fide* reason for not being able to fulfil the requirements. In that case, the committee would give them a further period of time to catch the hours up without being fined.

Now if somebody's playing the system and goes to the pub the night before, has too much to drink and doesn't turn up the next morning, he then has to make the hours up within a month and would also be fined. Hours can't be rolled on; they're added up to the last Sunday in each month. So if someone is in excess of the target hours in one month, he can't carry that forward to the next month.

How many hours a week are required?

MISS DRING: We reckon that a member coming into a scheme should get into his head between 14 and 30 hours a week. Obviously, in the summer-time, members are working long hours and taking advantage of the good weather – less in the winter.

They also work a couple of weeks of their main holidays on site, and bank holidays, Christmas—

—Christmas?

MISS DRING: Not Christmas day! And not New Year's day. They used to, but I found it was a total waste of time.

A person in a scheme becomes a specialist, don't they?

MISS DRING: They will eventually learn the skills. We've seen people change direction in occupations. There's a plumber in Kidderminster I remember. He joined the scheme as a DIY with a leaning towards plumbing, which is quite unusual – usually they lean towards carpentry, or building patios and that sort of thing. This chap had a real skill at plumbing; so he worked with the tradesman plumber of the scheme. At the end of the scheme, they went into partnership together, and he's now a plumber.

So a scheme can provide an opportunity to equip people with quite wide skills, which may enable them to secure better employment.

Is the decoration done personally, or is it like the other trades and some people are decorators for the whole scheme?

MISS DRING: It varies on every scheme.

Some people put extra money into the decorations and fitments because they want the best of everything.

When I go to the houses, I get a kick out of seeing the internal amendments that ladies have been involved in – the kitchen design, bathrooms. They've got some marvellous ideas. Sometimes I go on one of our sites, I go inside a house, and I can't recognize the house type. We allow them to move around non-loadbearing walls, and they're allowed to do a lot to personalize the house. We keep the construction economically sound, but inside they're allowed to personalize it to suit the family requirements.

What sort of certification do the houses get?

MISS DRING: We use architects' certificates. They do the design work. They're not in a strict supervisory capacity, but they inspect the site at stages and then issue the certificates when the scheme is completed.

With the Local Authority building inspectors we have nothing but good relations. When they discover that it's selfbuild and people are working for themselves, they take quite a paternal interest in the site. It's super. They always come to any site parties with their wives.

Do you have your own architects?

MISS DRING: Not internally, but we use one firm of architects. We've built up a library of house designs.

A lot of our work, as far as an architect and a solicitor is concerned, could be aborted. Nobody, including ourselves, receives any money until the scheme starts on site. Now any amount of work may have to be done to actually be able to place an offer. We may have to do tender drawings, all this sort of thing. So we found that commercially we had to encourage the architects to assist us to go forward, and they'd win some and lose some. So obviously the repetitive business helped. Our architects aren't paid the RIBA scale. It's a special selfbuild fee.

We've also found that their understanding of selfbuilders and the frustrations that emerge, the problems that may be encountered—

—were reflected in the design?

MISS DRING: No – the architects were needed on site construction. Sometimes, some of the most amazing things actually happen on site. They need the architect to come out and explain. The architects attend evening meetings of groups; they come out on sites at weekends. Not every architect is prepared to do that. So we found that by using one architect, the repeat business, the volume of business enables him to give the selfbuilders 150% service, which is what is needed. It's no use saying "Well, I can come out next week, on Friday" if the site has actually lost time.

It's the same with the solicitor. We use one firm of solicitors. They attend monthly meetings – not every one, depending on the agenda. They come and explain the land purchase contract, what the group are actually buying, what restrictions there are, covenants. They explain how the finance works. The members have to sign documents, obviously, and we believe that it's important that they understand the documents from the person who's actually dealing with them. And then at the end of the scheme, the solicitor is involved, obviously, in transferring the properties to the individual members; and he works with them on the legal side of mortgages, and all that sort of thing. So they have quite a high profile with the selfbuilders.

And because there is the volume there, presumably you get these legal services at a discount?

MISS DRING: You've got it!

At the end of the scheme, individual members have to buy their houses from the association, and the solicitors are currently charging them £100 for the conveyancing, which is tremendous. But it's bulk business. If you went outside you'd probably be paying £300, £400, whatever. And again, the solicitors now understand selfbuild.

Changing the subject a bit – do you do timber-frame schemes?

MISS DRING: Yes; we do.

We find them particularly an advantage for DIY selfbuild schemes. There are certain areas where there is not a prevalence of tradesmen. We have a fine example of a scheme in Stone, where we built some very nice houses. The *Daily Express* featured the scheme. That was made up almost entirely of middle-management people.

How did that come about?

MISS DRING: We promoted the scheme in the normal way – traditional selfbuild. But we found that we just weren't getting the tradesmen forward. We had a tremendous nucleus of very strong-minded people who wanted to do a selfbuild scheme but just didn't have the skills to assist them. So we actually talked to the group about abandoning the scheme – we thought it would be unfair to put them on the site with their present skills – and they point blank refused! "No way are you getting rid of us; we're going to do this scheme. Find some way for us to do it." So we said "Right, timber-frame has got to be the answer. We'll send several of you to the factory. You can see how the kits are made. We will provide supervision on site". Each time a kit arrived, the timber-frame company provided supervisory labour to work with the members to show how it was actually erected. We then provided a permanent site manager, on site, who was a practical man. He took them through all the other aspects. They carried out a lot themselves. The houses look like traditional houses. There's no sign from the outside at all that they're linked with timber-frame. They look wonderful.

So the advantage of timber-frame was that they're simpler to build?

MISS DRING: That's right. It cuts down on the subcontract element and reduces the costs.

Reduces the costs? In that case, why don't you do all timber-frame?

MISS DRING: It reduced the costs only in this particular scheme. Timber-frame is more expensive than traditional selfbuild, mainly because you're buying pre-manufactured components.

In a scheme where we have the normal trades input, traditional build is what the majority of selfbuilders want, and they can cope with the costs because they've got the labour from within. Whereas in a scheme where we were light on tradesmen, they would have to buy those in. So it was cheaper for them to do a timber-frame scheme.

Have you ever had any bad failures?

MISS DRING: No; degrees of success, but never a failure.

The houses have always been built, and they've never fallen down?

MISS DRING: No.

And have they always been built at below their market value when finished?

MISS DRING: Yes. As I say – degrees of success. But all the schemes have completed, all achieved their objectives.

You must have seen lots of mistakes being made on site?

MISS DRING: It would be very easy to sit back and say "That isn't the way to do it". But every group has to find their method of working – they're individuals joining collectively. And there are some jobs which are tackled the hard way round. But they need to go through that to gain the experience and confidence.

If you're talking about construction, there are times when we would say "That's got to come down. It's not satisfactory". We act as quality control to the nth degree. We're not talking about work the building inspector would pass. We're saying "This is not an acceptable standard for selfbuild. You are meant to be building to a good standard for yourselves". And in practice, in a scheme of 20 people, for every one man doing work he's got 19 supervising officers, because he's going to be doing the same job on their house. So in general, there are not a lot of problems on that basis at all.

Are there any points that you'd like to make?

MISS DRING: People may be interested in the funding of a scheme.

We use a variety of different funding agencies, about twelve. We acquire 100% of the developments costs, so the members need to put very little in. It's from building societies, banks, some merchant banks in London. Initially they advance the money for the land purchase, that's the first stage. From then on, the money is drawn down in monthly tranches. We complete certain returns, do valuations on site, do the paperwork, forward it to the financier – which equals, at the bottom line, "We want so much money". They send it to the group's bankers, which enables them to write cheques to pay their suppliers.

So that's how you manage to finance all these schemes?

MISS DRING: That's right.

And on completion of the scheme, a building society gives a mortgage to individual members?

MISS DRING: Yes.

We insist with the financiers involved that they do guarantee to all the members a mortgage at the end of the scheme, if the member wants it. There's no compulsion to take it. This stems from the days when there were mortgage queues, and people had to wait two or three months to actually secure a mortgage. This presented problems because, of course, every member must complete on the same day, repay the loan in its entirety to the financier. So we embarked on this arrangement, and the financiers are only too happy to provide mortgages. And usually the financier will provide what I refer to as a little package of goodies. If a financier has funded a scheme and their inspector has inspected the site, I see no reason why members should be paying a valuation fee for a mortgage at the end of the scheme. They've been looking at the scheme all the way through.

So somebody joining one of your schemes has to be eligible for a mortgage?

MISS DRING: Yes.

Or could somebody purchase their house from their own resources?

MISS DRING: Yes; we do have people who don't need a mortgage. Perhaps they're moving down, perhaps their families have grown up, perhaps they're moving to a smaller house.

What about people who need a mortgage but don't have a job? After all, they can put more hours in.

MISS DRING: We can actually secure mortgages for unemployed people.

But we found almost a market resistance to this. When we first organized this facility with the DHSS and the building society, we promoted it; this was at the time of the recession, particularly in the West Midlands.

Doesn't it make a lot of logic, if you're not working, to build a house?

MISS DRING: Absolutely. We argued with the DHSS that it wasn't employment, that they would be available for job interviews and all this sort of thing. And we promoted it to the public. But we found almost nil response. And we assumed that if someone is in long-term unemployment, there is a certain amount of apathy. But we've had people who in the course of a scheme have become unemployed.

What happens then?

MISS DRING: Well, they're guaranteed the mortgage – no problems there. What actually helps them is picking up the skills. They're able to look for a wider variety of jobs.

But we found, as I say, a market resistance in people who were unemployed before the scheme commenced, to come forward. Which we felt was very sad. We'd thought we'd found the hidden answer – "This is it, come here, get the skills, you can do this".

Is this still on offer?

MISS DRING: Yes.

Perhaps a lot of unemployed people wouldn't even think that they could build a home?

MISS DRING: This is why we embarked upon the marketing campaign. Either we failed, or they did. Yes; we thought it was ideal.

Do you find there are many differences between the Local Authorities towards selfbuild?

MISS DRING: Not nowadays. There used to be.

Some were keen, and others not?

MISS DRING: That's right. Some saw it as a means to reduce their waiting list for Council houses, to move people out from Council houses into owner-occupation, to free the Council houses for other people. I should think there are very few Local Authorities now who aren't aware how selfbuild works. It's taken a number of years to bring it to their attention. The problems nowadays in Local Authorities promoting a selfbuild scheme is they either

    a) haven't got the land,

  or b) they're empowered to sell it at the highest market value, which usually means going out to tender. In that, selfbuild sometimes isn't successful. In the past, they would say "We have identified this site for a selfbuild scheme". It was still for market value, but it was a private negotiation and much simpler to promote.

So you're not getting so much land from Local Authorities?

MISS DRING: They simply haven't got it.

When I first started, 99% of our land was from Local Authorities.

I think selfbuild has moved during the years that I've been involved. When I first started, it was almost regarded as one up from Council housing. The houses weren't the sort that people would choose to live in. They were boxes, semi-detached. "You mustn't have a coloured suite; it must be a plain, white suite." But over the years, it has moved across the whole spectrum, and the houses are actually now dream houses that people would want to go out and buy if they could afford it.

Selfbuild has more credibility now in the development world – builders, Local Authorities, and the like. It has a respectful taste to it these days. Whereas in the past, selfbuild – 'a bunch of amateurs, working in their spare time, some of them DIY, not tradesmen'. I could see the picture they were building up – sheer chaos. But now, with so many successful schemes around the country, people recognize it as an alternative way of acquiring new homes.

Do some groups carry on in some form after the completion of the scheme?

MISS DRING: Socially, yes; very much so – annual reunions. We have quite a social side to our selfbuild. We have site opening parties, tree planting ceremonies, handing over of keys, always a scheme completion party. Depending on the time of year, it might be a disco in the evening, or it might be a street party.

And do some of your people go to these?

MISS DRING: Whoever's free goes from the whole office.

You must get a bit *blasé* after a while?

MISS DRING: Oh, never. No; when you actually see a scheme completed and you look round at them and remember how they were when they first came in and what they've gone through – no; you don't ever become *blasé*.

It gives you satisfaction?

MISS DRING: Tremendous; yes.

It's a way of life, selfbuild. It's not just work. It's involved with people's aims, hopes, ambitions, frustrations. And there's a very strong family aspect to it.

GLOSSARY

Aggregate: Sand or stone, or both mixed together.

Architects' certificate: An architect periodically inspects a house as it is built and, if satisfied, certifies that it has been properly constructed. (Surveyors offer a similar service.) Building societies need such a certificate before making a mortgage to a selfbuilder.

Architrave: Wooden strips around a door opening which hide any crack between the door lining and the wall.

Baluster: Banister.

Barge board: The board which hides and protects the gable ladder; it follows the slope of the roof. There are two at a gable end, meeting together in a point at the ridge.

Barge foot: An extra piece added to a barge board in order to block off the gap where the barge board meets the soffit of the eaves.

Bonding: The pattern of the mortar joints in brickwork (or block-work).

Browning: A Gypsum plaster (i.e., similar to Plaster of Paris), pre-mixed with lightweight material to bulk it out. Used for the floating coat (i.e., undercoat) of plasterwork. (See also 'Render'.)

Cement: A powder, usually grey, which forms a paste with water that sets hard. It is invariably mixed with aggregate to give concrete, mortar, render, etc.

Concrete: Made by mixing cement, stone, sand and water. Their proportions can be varied: the more cement, the stronger and more expensive the concrete. Common mixes are 4:2:1 and 6:3:1 (stone : sand : cement). Used for foundations, solid floors, paths, etc.

Corbel: A projection from a wall that supports a load above it. Necessary with flush verges to support the small area of gable projecting beyond the main wall; often built in stepped-out brick-work.

Course: A course in brickwork is a level layer of bricks.

Door lining: At internal door openings, boards hide the edges of the wall and support the door. (At external door openings, door frames are used instead.)

Dpc: Damp proof course. Wide plastic 'ribbon' laid along the base of a wall to prevent rising damp.

Dpm: Damp proof membrane. Plastic sheeting laid beneath a concrete floor to prevent rising damp.

Dry lining: Finishing wall surfaces with plasterboard. Necessary with timber-frame construction and studwork. An alternative to plastering on blockwork.

Eaves: The lowest part of a roof where it overhangs its supporting wall.

Fascia: The board that protects and hides the bottom ends of rafters or roof trusses. Often carries a gutter, hence its alternative name of 'gutter board'.

Fatty: Refers to the composition and feel of a wet mix of mortar, concrete, render, etc. A fatty mix is rich in small particles and feels cohesive and easy to work.

Felt and battening: Slaters' felt is used on a pitched roof beneath the tiles as a second line of defence against the weather. It is fixed in place with rows of battens, which also support the tiles.

Finial: A vertical ornament in timber, occasionally found at the top of barge boards, hanging down from stair newels on landings, etc.

Finish plaster: Plaster used for skimming. (See 'Skim'.)

Flashing: Material (usually lead) used to cover the joint between a wall and roof.

Float: A type of trowel used to make plaster or concrete flat and smooth. (Can also be a verb: to use the float.)

Floating coat: The thick undercoat of plaster which flattens out the irregularities of the wall beneath it. On internal work, it's finished off with a skim coat.

Flush verge: See 'Verge'.

Frog: A hollow in the top (or bottom!) of some types of brick.

Gable: The triangle of walling contained beneath the two slopes of a pitched roof. (A hipped roof, however, has only eaves and no gable.)

Gable ladder: Timber framework that carries the roof out over a gable. (See 'Verge'.)

Gobbo: Mortar (slang). Also called **compo**.

Hod: A V-shaped container used for carrying bricks and mortar on the shoulder.

Joints: In brickwork, this refers to the spaces between the bricks that are filled with mortar: bed-joints (horizontal) and cross-joints (vertical).

Joists: Beams for supporting a floor or ceiling.

Kite: Found sometimes where stairs turn a corner. In addition to winders, one of the treads may be shaped like a kite (i.e., a squashed diamond shape). (See 'Winders'.)

Laying to the line: In bricklaying, two corners are first put up, and then a line, stretched tight between them, is used to guide the laying of the brickwork in between.

Leaf: A cavity wall combines a leaf of brickwork and a leaf of blockwork, separated by a gap (usually 5 cm) but tied together at intervals by wall ties.

Lintel: A beam (nowadays steel) which supports the brickwork above a door or window opening.

Low-emissive glass: Glass with a transparent coating on one face; it reflects radiant heat back into a warm room.

Matchboard: Tongue-and-grooved board with a decorative 'V' channel along the joint.

Mortar: Mixture of cement, sand and water (sometimes with lime also), which is used for sticking bricks together.

Mortise: A traditional way to join two pieces of wood is with a mortise-and-tenon joint. The mortise is the rectangular hole, and the tenon fits into it.

Motorized valve: An electrically-operated valve controlling the flow in central-heating pipework.

Noggings: The short cross-pieces of timber used to make up studwork. (See 'Studwork'.)

Overhand: Usually a bricklayer works from the front of the brickwork he's laying, i.e., so he's looking at its fair face. Sometimes he has to work from the back and lay 'overhand', which is slower.

Oversite: The concrete base laid over the plan area of the house.

Plate: A wall plate is a length of timber running along the top of a wall to support roof trusses (or rafters). A sole plate is a length of timber fixed to the floor and to which studwork, timber-frame panels, etc., can be attached.

Profiles: These are used to transfer the plan outline of a building onto the ground. They are boards about a metre long fixed in place by a couple of stakes. By stretching a line tight between marks on a pair of profiles, the position for a wall can be fixed.

Purlin: Found in traditional roof construction. It is a strong beam which supports rafters about midway up the slope.

Render: A sand-and-cement mix used for plastering, either outside or as the floating coat inside – although for this, browning is more popular.

Rodding eye: To give access for rodding a drain, a short length of drain pipe slopes down from the ground surface into the drain. Its cover at ground level is elliptical (i.e., shaped like an eye, and hence, perhaps, the name).

Screed: A sand-and-cement 'plaster' applied to a floor rather than a wall to make it flat and smooth. Also has a second meaning: fillets of plaster or wood, called 'screeds', are used to divide up a wall to give true levels for plastering (or divide a floor for screeding).

Scrim: Cloth (rather like first-aid bandage) which is used to cover the joints between plasterboards before skimming. This prevents the skim coat from cracking later.

Setting out: Marking out cn the ground the plan area of the house to be built. This involves putting up the profiles.

Sharp: Sharp sand is coarse and suitable for making concrete. Soft sand contains more fine particles and is suitable for mortar.

Skim: In plasterwork, the skim coat is the topcoat, i.e., a thin coat of finish plaster with a smooth surface. (Also used as a verb: to apply the finish coat.)

Skip float: A wide, flat plate on a long pole. Used to smooth off the surface of wet concrete without anybody having to stand in it.

Soffit: A flat under-surface, e.g., beneath the eaves.

Sole plate: See 'Plate'.

Stack: The soil pipe that runs from the top of the house, where air can be sucked into it, down to the drain. Individual soil pipes from WC's, and waste pipes from basins etc., run into it.

Stage payments: Benign building societies make their loans available in instalments as the build progresses. A typical arrangement would be a quarter of the full loan at: foundations; roof on; plastered; finished.

Strip foundations: A trench is dug, say 60 cm wide and deep. The bottom is covered with concrete to a depth of 15 cm, and the walls are built up off this. (Compare 'Trench-fill foundations'.)

Studwork: Timber framework, usually covered with plasterboard to make a wall. The studs are the vertical members from floor to ceiling. They ,are stiffened with short horizontal pieces called noggings.

Topping out: A ceremony that celebrates the construction of the highest part of a building. Traditionally, it includes the flying of the Union Jack and drinks all round!

Transom: A horizontal cross-member of a window frame, dividing the window into parts.

Trench-fill foundations: A deeper and narrower trench is used than for strip foundations (say, a metre deep and 45 cm wide). This is filled with concrete nearly up to ground level. A fast but unecological method.

Trusses: Triangular frames used in the construction of a roof. Prefabricated in a factory for an individual house. (The traditional way of constructing a roof *in situ* is rarely used nowadays.)

Two-and-one gang: Bricklayers usually work in pairs, one from each corner, with a labourer supplying them with bricks and mortar.

Verge: Edge of the roof at a gable end. The fashion in the Sixties and Seventies was to project the verge out over the gable with a gable ladder. The contemporary fashion is for a flush verge: the roof projects only a few centimetres beyond the gable.

U-value: Gives a measure of the rate at which heat is lost through some particular component of a building. The lower the better.

Vac-vac treatment: For the deep impregnation of timber with preservative. A vacuum is used to suck the air out of timber. This is then immersed in preservative which is sucked into it. The vacuum is applied again to remove surplus preservative.

Wall plate: See 'Plate'.

Winders: If there is sufficient space, the best way to turn a corner on a staircase is with a landing. If the flight itself has to turn, the triangular shaped treads are called winders. (See also 'Kite'.)

Window board: Popularly called the window sill, though technically the sill is the bottom member of the window frame.

Yorkshire fittings: Bends and the like used in copper pipework. Their distinctive feature is that they contain their own solder, and so are easy for amateurs to use.

SOURCES OF FURTHER INFORMATION

Books:

BRICK BY BRICK: the Leading Edge guide to building your own home
ISBN 0 948135 10 7   £6–25
First published 1989, by Leading Edge Press and Publishing.
A good introduction to the many options possible in selfbuild.
Covers the managerial rather than the manual aspects.

BUILDING YOUR OWN HOME by Murray Armor
ISBN 1 85327 028 8   £6–95
11th Edition 1988, by Prism Press.
A popular perennial, covering the story of the selfbuild movement.
Lots of case histories with smiling faces.

PRACTICAL HOUSE BUILDING: a manual for the selfbuilder by
Robert Matthews
ISBN 0 9515295 1 X   £12–50
First published May 1990, by Blackberry Books.
A comprehensive guide to conventional house building for the
selfbuilder, covering all stages from finding a plot to decorating.

THE SELF-BUILDER by Nicholas Snelgar
ISBN 0 7153 8765 0   £12–95
First published 1987, by David and Charles.
A practical but rather brief guide to traditional house building.

COHOUSING by Kathryn McCamant and Charles Durrett
ISBN 0 945929 29 3   £14–50
First published 1988, by Habitat Press.
An American book of Danish examples of co-operative housing
schemes. A delightful inspiration of how our lives could so simply
be so much richer. If you are forming a selfbuild group, why not
continue co-operation when the building has finished?

Periodicals:

THE SELF-BUILDER
£1 for two issues, from Homesmith plc, 'Northfield', Snelsins Road,
Cleckheaton, West Yorkshire, BD19 3EU.
Mainly about managed selfbuild projects.

MUTUAL NEWS
£15 an issue, from Mutual Land Developments Ltd, Freepost, Hereford HR1 3BR.
Contains details of building plots nationwide. Send also for their package-build brochure.

☆   ☆   ☆   ☆   ☆

Courses:

CONSTRUCTIVE INDIVIDUALS
1 The Cottages, Hambleton, Selby, North Yorkshire, YO8 9JE.
Practical building course, using a modular timber-frame technique specially designed for selfbuild.

JUVAN COURSES
Freepost, Longhope, Gloucestershire, GL17 0AA.
Weekend courses in plastering, etc.

CENTRE FOR ALTERNATIVE TECHNOLOGY
Pantperthog, near Machynlleth, Powys, Wales, SY20 9AZ.
Weekend courses in the Segal method of selfbuild, solar energy, etc.

For particular trades, try adult-education day or evening classes; or technical colleges. Look out for TV programs (especially in winter) covering DIY techniques.

☆   ☆   ☆   ☆   ☆

Info Centres:

BUILDING CENTRES:
Containing books, exhibitions and manufacturers' information.
26 STORE ST, LONDON, WC1E 7BT.
Colston Avenue, Bristol, BS1 4TW.
15 Trumpington St, Cambridge, CB2 1QD.
C/O NFBTE, Green Lane, Durham, DH1 3JI.
3 Claremont Terrace, Glasgow, G3 7PF.
113 Portland St, Manchester, M1 6FB.
18 Cumberland Pace, Southampton, SO1 2BD.

OTHER BOOKSHOPS:
Design Centre, 28 Haymarket, London, SW1Y 4SU.
Housing Centre Bookshop, 33 Alfred Place, London, WC1E 7DP.
Planning Bookshop, 17 Carlton House Terrace, London, SW1Y 5AH.
Stobart and Son, 67 Worship St, London, EC2A 2EL.

ROYAL INSTITUTE OF BRITISH ARCHITECTS (RIBA)
66 Portland Place, London, W1N 4AD.
The very useful library is open for reference to the general public.
There is also a bookshop.

INTERBUILD EXHIBITION
National Exhibition Centre, Birmingham.
November, but only odd-numbered years.
The largest of any British exhibition.

WALTER SEGAL SELF-BUILD TRUST
PO Box 542, London, SE1 1TX.
The trust promotes the post-and-beam method of selfbuild
pioneered by architect, Walter Segal. This method can be quickly
mastered by anyone without prior building experience. The trust
can also advise on setting up a selfbuild group.
For a description of Segal's method, see Architects' Journal, 5th
November 1986.

THE NATIONAL FEDERATION OF HOUSING ASSOCIATIONS
Warwickgate House, Warwick Road, Manchester, M16 0DD.
Give advice on forming selfbuild housing associations. Their book
Selfbuild (£6–95) suggests fair working arrangements for selfbuild
groups. They also publish a list of selfbuild consultants.

THE COMMUNITY SELFBUILD AGENCY LTD
Room 5.22, 149 Tottenham Court Road, London, W1P 0BN.
A collaboration of the Housing Corporation with private businesses. The Agency promotes the formation of selfbuild groups for
people 'in housing need'.

☆   ☆   ☆   ☆   ☆

House-Building Packages

For conventional construction:

DESIGN AND MATERIALS LTD
Carlton Industrial Estate, Worksop, Nottinghamshire, S81 9LB.

RATIONALISED BUILDING SYSTEMS LTD
Unit 29, Argyle Industrial Estate, Heol Trelai, Cardiff, CF5 5NJ.

For prefabricated timber-frame:

BRISTOL TIMBER FRAME LTD
Hope Chapel House, Hope Chapel Hill, Hotwells, Bristol, BS8 4ND.

GUILDWAY LTD
Old Portsmouth Road, Guildford, Surrey, GU3 1LR.

PRESTOPLAN LTD
Stanley Street, Preston, Lancashire, PR1 4AT.
3 Dunlop Street, Strathaven, Lanarkshire, Scotland, ML10 6LA.
153 Upper Newtonwards Road, Belfast, BT4 3HX.

PURPOSE BUILT LTD
Spring Lane South, Malvern Link, Worcestershire, WR14 1AQ.

and several others.

☆   ☆   ☆   ☆   ☆

Building Societies

NATIONAL AND PROVINCIAL BUILDING SOCIETY
Offer 100% mortgages which include the plot price.

BIRMINGHAM MIDSHIRES BUILDING SOCIETY
Offer a 'roll-on' mortgage: the self builder can have their old house mortgaged (and so live in it) while they build the new one.